In the Lyme-Light II

Portraits of Illness and Healing

D1595559

Emily Bracale

I dedicate this book to Kirsten Stockman
who comforted and encouraged me
in my darkest of times with Lyme.
Though no longer in her body
she invites our attention to
remember the spiritual
reality in which we
are all healed
and all truly
one.
༅

Self Published by Emily Bracale
Maine Authors Publishing
558 Main Street
Rockland, ME 04841

Copyright 2014 by Emily Bracale
Foreword copyright 2014 by Patricia L. Gerbarg, M.D.

ISBN: 978-1-938883-94-1

cover art by Emily Bracale: Cloister Walk–watercolor, oil pastel, birch bark, gold leaf, collage papers, 26.75" x 34.5", 2007

Artwork

1. White Lights — 8
2. Lyme-aid — 10
3. "Fine, thanks!" — 12
4. Depression — 14
5. Rock Bottom — 15
6. One Step at a Time — 17
7. Fluff and Icebergs — 19
8. Permanent Records — 21
9. Bar Code — 24
10. Mad Math — 26
11. Strength as Weakness — 28
12. Half an Apple — 30
13. Remember? — 32
14. Brain Fog — 34
15. The Central Nervous System — 36
16. Party Pooper — 38
17. It's All in Your Head — 40
18. Asphyxiation — 42
19. Poor Mother Deer — 43

20. Fight/Flight — 45
21. Insomnia — 46
22. Sleep – Assembly Instructions — 48
23. Helping Hands — 49
24. Side Effects — 51
25. Path of Recovery — 53
26. 63 Days — 55
27. Healing Supports — 57
28. Mind Sets — 59
29. Letting Go — 61

30. Standing in Both Worlds — 65
31. Particles and Waves — 69
32. Heart Opening — 72
33. Memorial with Rose Petals — 75
34. Healing Within a Lotus — 78
35. Tree of Trauma and Fear — 80
36. Eye into Nothing — 82
37. Cloister Walk — 85

Foreword

My first reactions to *In the Lyme-Light* were surprise, recognition, and gratitude. I was surprised by the eloquence of Emily's visual images and the beauty in her description of the devastating effects of Lyme disease on her mind, body, and spirit. Those of us who have lived with Lyme disease, who have struggled to understand and express what we experience, recognize exactly what Emily portrays in words and colors. And with that recognition comes a sense of gratitude that someone has found a way to tell our story, to convey the many nuances of denying, resisting, hiding, self-doubting, trying, loving, learning, adapting, and eventually coping with a mysterious and widely misunderstood illness.

As a physician, my concerns about Lyme disease began as I saw the number of deer increase every year in our neighborhood. Like many families, we had a little dog, Rocky. Like many pets Rocky wore a pest repellent collar and still brought deer ticks into our house. Being a conscientious mother, I meticulously removed Rocky's ticks and scoured the house for any that might have fallen off, never thinking that I might be the one to get bitten.

As with Emily, Lyme took its time creeping into my system causing a little soreness here, a little stiffness there and gradually over about five years, more and more pain, weakness, exhaustion, and mental clouding. Emily's painting, "Rock Bottom," says it all. When you are curled up in bed for hours waiting for the pain to stop, unable to think clearly, fighting off fears that you might never get your life back, fending off doubts that this could all be in your head, feeling guilty about being sick…you are just a rock at the bottom of an endless dark sea.

Although Lyme devastated my life during the last two years of my illness, I consider myself lucky because an infectious disease specialist finally diagnosed the condition based on a SPECT scan of my brain, that is a special scan that showed where the narrowing of blood vessels (from Lyme organisms invading the inner lining) was reducing blood flow to critical brain areas. After nine months of antibiotic treatment I began what is now about 15 years of post-Lyme gradual recovery. Although the antibiotics were necessary to eradicate the infection, they did not repair the damage it had done to the cells of my brain, muscles and tendons. Antibiotics did not stop the inflammatory process that is much quieter now, but that still smolders in my tendons and that is too easily evoked by any strenuous activity. Fortunately, my husband, Dr. Richard Brown, had developed considerable expertise in complementary treatments. One of the herbs he tried, *Rhodiola rosea**, restored my balance, memory, and other cognitive functions. Some of the medicinal compounds in the roots of this herb enhance cellular energy production and repair. Discovering the benefits of this herb was the genesis of my interest in complementary and alternative medicine. This led to an entirely new direction in my career and the many rewards of being able to heal people who could not respond to other treatments. With *Rhodiola rosea*, other supplements, and mind-body practices, I am still not able to do everything I used to do, but I can do anything that is really important for me, my family, and my work.

One of my favorite pictures is Emily's "Pillows." It reminded me of the nine pillows I used to need in order to sleep during the worst of times. It made me laugh and feel good about the fact that now I only need two.

When Lyme infection is recognized quickly, a three-week course of antibiotics is usually all that is needed. However, only about 40% of people bitten by ticks develop the tell-tale bull's-eye rash and only about 70% show positive results on standard blood tests for Lyme. That leaves thousands who may not know they were bitten or whose cases were untreated owing to false negative tests. Many of these people are at risk for developing long term complications including chronic pain, inflammation, fatigue, insomnia, cognitive slowing, memory loss, incoordination, loss of balance, brain damage, heart damage, paralysis of nerves, digestive problems, rashes, and more. Lyme disease is the Great Pretender. Since the microorganisms can invade any tissues anywhere in the body, the damage they cause can mimic many other illnesses. When a patient has odd symptoms that don't fit into a standard pattern, doctors may assume that the problem is psychological.

Now that I have become a "Lyme literate" psychiatrist, many Lyme patients are sent to me because their medical doctors believe that their symptoms are psychosomatic, that is, "all in the patient's head." Well, some of the symptoms may be in the patient's head because that is one of the favorite locations for Lyme spirochetes. For example, an infectious disease doctor treated a college student with Lyme disease for one month with antibiotics. After stopping the

---

*Rhodiola rosea, the stonecrop Golden root, has not gone through the process that would be necessary to obtain approval from the US Food and Drug Administration to treat or prevent disease. In other countries in Europe and Scandinavia, *R. rosea* has been part of the approved pharmacopeia for decades.

antibiotics, the doctor sent this student to see me because he was having mood swings and acting strangely. A brain scan showed a long, thin cavity in the brain tissue in the right cerebral hemisphere. The other doctor thought it might have been caused by an unknown brain injury. However, there was no history of brain injury and the cavity was nowhere near any of the brain areas that are damaged during most kinds of head trauma. By reminding my colleague that infections in brain cavities are highly resistant to antibiotics, I was able to persuade him to resume and maintain the antibiotics. Within a week, the patient began to recover.

Two of the most essential ingredients for Lyme recovery are to develop a fighting spirit and a way to transform the experience, to make it part of your pattern of personal growth so that it enriches your life. As with anything that is an unwanted part of us, the more we avoid, deny, reject, and hate it, the more it drains our spirit. Seeing Lyme for what it is, accepting that it is an integral part of our existence, and using all of our awareness, insight, and creative energy to learn from it and to ultimately transform the experience and ourselves is the deeper message within this book. This is the "Letting Go," the letting go of one's natural fearful, defensive reaction to pain and suffering in order to explore the possibilities of creating an existence you never envisioned for yourself. By sharing her story, Emily the teacher leads us to the question, "Can we find a way through our disease to live a better life and nurture the spirit of love within ourselves and those who are dear to us?"

I hope that readers will share this book with as many people as possible, not only to heighten awareness and understanding for those who live with Lyme, but also because prevention is one of the best weapons we have in fighting what is currently a losing battle against the growing epidemic of Lyme. For example, in places where vigorous public education about Lyme prevention was implemented the number of new Lyme cases dropped by as much as 70%.

Medical debates, battles over insurance coverage for antibiotics, absence of serious public health initiatives, attacks on doctors who recognize and treat chronic Lyme, and lack of accurate tests and effective treatments all contribute to the private and public burden of this disease. Many Lyme patients are left with no doctor, no insurance coverage, and no treatment as their illness relentlessly progresses. Sometimes families who cannot understand the illness or who cannot bear to be around the person who is ill, abandon their loved one, leaving him or her without financial, physical, or emotional support. I believe that this book will contribute to the growing literature on Lyme disease, not only as an artistic statement, but also as a medium that may open people's eyes and hearts to the inner world of those who are experiencing a life-changing illness.

My hope is that as more people come to understand the impact of Lyme on all of our lives, the tide will turn in the direction of more enlightened education, treatment, and prevention. I just want to thank Emily for sharing her extraordinary book with me.

Patricia L. Gerbarg, M.D.
Assistant Professor of Clinical Psychiatry
New York Medical College
Co-author of "How to Use Herbs, Nutrients and Yoga in Mental Health Care" (W.W. Norton, 2009)
www.haveahealthymind.com

Preface

My first book, *In the Lyme-Light: Portraits of Illness and Healing*, was published in 2011. This new edition includes the revised and updated story as well as *Further Reflections on Healing*. The original twenty-eight paintings are joined by nine new works of art, printed larger and brighter to convey the experience of viewing them in a gallery, as was originally intended. I joyfully share my story of healing from Lyme in the spirit of helping other people find the understanding, advocacy, encouragement, and support they need for their own healing.

This project began in 2009 as a private artistic exploration. Like many people with Lyme disease, my health had been rocky for years. By early 2009 my physical, social, personal, financial, and professional life had all "bottomed out." Even my lifelong love of making art was gone. It felt as if my old life was over, but I couldn't see any future. Something felt terribly wrong, but I didn't suspect that Lyme disease was part of it. I knew very little about the disease – I assumed things and heard of people getting it, but never bothered to ask what that entailed.

That spring, through a series of fortunate events, I began to suspect that I might have Lyme – and possibly had for half my life! I began a crash course in learning about the disease and how to self-advocate for the treatment I needed. I was astonished to learn how serious it could become and, moreover, that it is a subject of incredible controversy. I began trying to share what I was going through with family, friends, and doctors, cautiously revealing some of the darker side of my life for the first time. Talking with other Lyme patients let me know that I was going down the right path. After asking about my symptoms, one called me a "poster child" for Lyme and told me to seek medical help immediately. Finding out about Lyme disease was frightening, but it was also an epiphany. It explained so much. I felt as if I were waking up from a long and crazy nightmare.

When ideas for this art and writing began coming to mind I knew I was in recovery. Having been an artist, writer, and teacher for most of my life, it was natural to turn to paints, words, and stories to come to terms with my experience of illness. One evening after a long hot bath I jotted down a whole page of inspired notes describing how to illustrate symptoms symbolically. This creative project turned my attention toward affirming life. But there was still fatigue, contending with medications and their side effects, two part-time jobs, and endless household tasks as a single parent of a preschooler and a

teenager. At some point, feeling too flat, gray, and overwhelmed "to ever be creative again," I threw the list away.

Then, in January of 2010, the urge to paint came back in force – almost compelling me to respond, no matter how tired and achy I still felt. When I let go of trying to figure out how to do anything and just showed up, so did the inspiration! I also felt strongly that my story was to be shared to help other people. Even if there were controversies about Lyme, I could share my own subjective experience, and as an artist provide a window into the experience for others to consider. The art that emerged was different from any I'd done before. Most of my work had been watercolor landscapes and sketches documenting places where I had traveled. The new work portrayed internal landscapes and internal journeys. Many images held meaning beyond what I was aware of to begin with, and humor beyond what I felt consciously capable of inventing. I found myself laughing out loud as if it were someone else's ideas I was discovering, tapping into that delightful zone of being the radio, broadcasting songs, instead of trying to be the station, figuring out what to play.

As I experienced the creation of each piece and studied them, it became clear that some written explanations were necessary. There was a sense of being wisely guided about what to share, for which I was grateful. With over forty years of life experience, there were many possible themes that I might have incorporated into a memoir – not all as dramatic as the Lyme theme, some much more comfortable for my ego to disclose! Any time I questioned the wisdom of revealing so much detail from my private (and often uncomfortable) experiences, I sensed an inner "green light" to continue. This was a hugely satisfying process of expression and discovery.

Just two months later, at the end of February 2010, twenty-six paintings and eighteen pages of notes became the first Lyme-Light exhibit, held at College of the Atlantic's Blum Gallery, in Bar Harbor, Maine. The exhibit was a "coming out" experience. Much of what I shared was news to my family, friends, and neighbors. People had known me as a student at the College of the Atlantic, a teacher, a parent, and an artist who painted landscapes. Now I revealed publicly what I had recently been afraid to admit even to myself. The outcome was deeply affirming. Many people said that my story resonated with their own experiences. The bizarre descriptions and images I shared met with grateful exclamations of recognition. Several people decided to get tested or seek treatment.

The art exhibit went on tour to many libraries in Maine and two in Vermont. Friends created a website for the project, and many people suggested turning the exhibit into a book. Since publishing that book in early 2011, I have heard from hundreds of people who said that my story gave voice to their own. Some donated the book to their local clinics and libraries. Encountering the work helped some people realized they had Lyme, others alerted friends or relatives whom they came to suspect had it, and now many more people are on the path of healing instead of being mired in some "mystery illness."

Meanwhile, as I had anticipated, the epidemic still grows. Every day there are new stories about long misdiagnosed cases, people going into debt paying for treatments, doctors being uninformed or unwilling to treat it, or treatments working but doctors being sued, and so much conflicting information! It's easy to feel frustrated, frightened, outraged, confused, and helpless in the face of all this. I feel the deepest sympathy and compassion for those who are still down in the mire of symptoms, too enmeshed to imagine a way through. But you are not alone, and there may be new support which you can yet find. I believe more than ever that *some healing is possible for all who make that their deepest intention in life* – not only physical healing, but also healing of heart and mind.

When I published my first book I was still fairly disabled, though making progress. Now, in spite of having had Lyme for half of my life, I now feel more well-being than ever. My cognitive clarity is reliable enough to confidently work as a private academic tutor and to homeschool my son. I again enjoy painting *plein air* landscapes and seascapes and teaching art classes. Some things I thought I would never do again, such as play clarinet, in an orchestra, are part of my daily and weekly rhythm. I could just be "one of the lucky ones," but I believe more healing has come from purposefully embracing and surrendering to transformation rather than from just fighting against an illness and trying to reconstitute the life I had.

While this book focuses on Lyme disease, it certainly also touches on dynamics of illness and healing that could apply to other illnesses. Illnesses take place on many levels simultaneously. Through facing Lyme I touched down into all the areas of my life that were neglected and in need of healing: physically, emotionally, mentally, socially, and spiritually. This has been, and continues to be, an immensely powerful process of transformation on all levels. Getting medical treatment was essential, but the inner psychological or spiritual work of inquiry, mindfulness, and contemplation were also involved to go this next stretch. By now I have learned and grown and benefitted

from the healing journey so deeply that it is impossible to see myself as a victim of Lyme any more; instead, more of a student.

A story on the side: while my daughter was still in high school she enrolled in a college class. As her work earned her credit toward high school graduation, credit was also applied toward a college-level diploma. I share this to make the point that what it takes to heal from Lyme may likewise earn us these "dual credits." The process of healing from Lyme may engage us in a personal, psychological, and spiritual journey that goes beyond altering our physical health. We may also discover that we are becoming more open minded, open hearted, conscious, present, and awake. The second part of this new book, *Further Reflections on Healing*, explores more directly what the first book gently suggested: the possibility of *transformative* healing.

Emily Bracale
Bar Harbor, Maine
March 24, 2014

1. White Lights
acrylic on canvas
11" x 14", 2009

1. White Lights

White Lights was my first attempt to portray Lyme symptoms visually. The landscape represented my memory, my history, my daily experience in private and public, the "landscape of my life" as it were. The foggy patches of white light were meant to obscure that scene, representing loss of memory, loss of functionality, and loss of the ability to see clearly and plan where I was going in life. But, as you might already see for yourself, when I looked at the painting again, from a distance, there were other symbolic interpretations of the white patches. Floating lights? Fireflies? Fairies? Angels? Beings of light? Spirit guides? Holes in the fabric of time and space? Portals into another dimension, holes where the light of heaven shines through, appearing as stars? Flashes of insight and inspiration? There is always more than one way to see things!

2. Lime-aid

"If life gives you limes, make limeade." This illustration is a metaphor for many things: it refers to the therapeutic act of transforming my difficult experiences of Lyme disease into art and words that communicate to and aid other people. The contents of the bag could also represent donations of time, money, and support from friends and family helping me with personal expenses and supporting this Lyme-Light project.

Some people call it "Lymes," but it's officially "Lyme" disease. That name comes from the place, Lyme, Connecticut, where a woman like me started asking questions, telling her stories, and believing that more attention and support were needed for the strange illness suddenly afflicting so many people in her community. The term "Lyme disease" can refer to one species of bacteria, *Borrelia burgdorferi (Bb)*, which has many different strains and is a cousin of syphilis. (In some reports it is called "deer syphilis.") It can be passed to humans and other mammals through the bite of certain ticks and is also known to be spread by migrating birds such as Canada Geese. Pets can also bring ticks into the home. Some studies discuss other methods of *Bb* transmission via mosquitos and fleas, and by gestational and sexual transmission from person to person. By now cases of Lyme have been reported in all states and in many countries around the world. Some reports consider *Bb* infection to be a global epidemic.

The term "Lyme disease" is also (inaccurately) used more broadly to refer to the varied cocktail of other tick-borne diseases (TBDs) a person may acquire from a bite, such as Anaplasma, Bartonella, Ehrlichiosis, and Babesiosis, the last a protozoan disease similar to malaria. These may also be referred to as "co-infections." Furthermore, it is hypothesized that an immune system compromised by *Bb* and other TBDs may be vulnerable to other infections, such as yeast infections and chronic herpes outbreaks, which have nothing to do with ticks or *Bb*, but these may *also* be referred to as "co-infections." One chronic illness might upset a person's hormonal balances, which in turn might lead to other illnesses. In an immune-compromised body, a "passing" cold might take root and last for months. The situation can become a complicated mess – both symptomatically and verbally!

The good news is that not all ticks are carriers, not everyone bitten becomes ill, and some who do may heal on their own; it is not necessarily going to develop into a chronic disease. But it is important to become more educated about the signs and symptoms. Two of the greatest risk factors in getting a chronic, costly, and debilitating case of Lyme disease are denial – of its potential severity or even existence – and lack of awareness and prevention. The sooner the disease is suspected, diagnosed, and treated, the better and cheaper the outcome is for everyone. But we're still in the pioneering phase. The common blood tests are not always accurate. A person may be very ill and have Lyme, but get a negative blood test for many reasons. Until recently, I, like many people, did not realize that Lyme disease could be so serious nor that I was at high risk of exposure to it. Anyone who plays outside in nature, gardens, hikes, or sits out in grassy fields painting, as I often used to do, is a potential candidate for Lyme.

For more information I recommend the website for ILADS: the International Lyme and Associated Diseases Society, at www.ilads.org.

2. Lime-aid
acrylic on birch
16" x 20", 2010

3. "Fine, thanks!"

In March, 2009, when I turned forty-two, I made my first appointment in six years for a routine physical. "How are you?" my new doctor asked. "Fine," I replied politely, same as to most people in passing. I did mention having trouble sleeping, feeling worn down, having roving aches and pains, becoming easily agitated and irritable. But I said all this kind of "off to the side," muffled by self-conscious embarrassment. After all, what single mother of two home-schooled kids (preschool and teen) after five months of a Maine winter isn't a bit frazzled? I was wary of coming across as a complainer.

Many people who think they have Lyme have a difficult time getting support and treatment. Some are told that they are imagining part or all of the predicament. Some are resigned to treating Lyme as an unfortunate lifelong affliction that they must just cope with. Some are told they have a mental illness or emotional issues in need of counseling and therapy. What stands out about my story is that I was the one who tried to make the disease be "all in my head" for so many years, treating my symptoms as psychosomatic side effects of stress and "personal issues." I ignored the escalating severity of physical and neurological problems until there was considerable damage to the nervous system and a compromised immune system.

Privately my life consisted of treading water from minute to minute, hour to hour. Getting the kids breakfast, getting through to lunch time, making it to dinner, finally lying down but not sleeping well; too much anxiety, weird electrical buzzing sensations, crazy unfocused thoughts, and chronic physical pain. I frequently felt so miserable that I wanted to leave my body. At a rare outing with other moms and kids I casually mentioned just wanting to "walk away from it all," referring delicately to suicide. "Don't we all?" someone replied. I didn't say anything more.

There is a silencing process inherent in having an undiagnosed chronic illness. If you have an acute case of flu you stay in bed, don't brush your hair, let the raggedness show. Anyone could tell that you are ill. But when the feeling of being ill goes on for weeks, months, years – waxing and waning in erratic cyclical patterns – you learn to somehow carry on to the best of your ability. You get dressed up for work, brush your hair, put on a social smile. There are bills to pay, children to raise, friends and neighbors with more acute surgeries and chemotherapy appointments that seem more substantially serious. If at times you acknowledge the depth of the physical pain you are enduring, your mind gone madly blank or streaming with hallucinations, the fact that you feel like crying all the time and some times do (when there is a private moment – it's like peeing; you can wait, but it's gotta come out sometime) – you can start to question your own sanity around it. Are you, in fact, going crazy? A hypochondriac? A lazy person looking for excuses? Or, worst of all, are you committing some kind of New Age error by *manifesting* all this instead of good health?

My symptoms confused me. Sometimes I was fine for a few weeks. I often thought it was because I was doing something right: eating the right food, getting enough sun and exercise, thinking positive thoughts, finding the right combination of prayers, affirmations, and vitamins. Then, for no apparent reason, I'd get wrung out again: mentally, emotionally, and physically. I suspected arthritis, chronic fatigue, and fibromyalgia, but friends and family with those conditions didn't seem to be getting lasting relief by going to their doctors, so I didn't bother pursuing treatment for those. There were some rashes, but I thought they were poison ivy or Shingles, and figuring that the latter was an untreatable virus I just made due with over the counter remedies. Once I went for a pelvic exam because of feeling the most excruciating pain in my life –as if a barbed knitting needle were poking up my spine – and was told I had a vaginal yeast infection. Soon, as usual, blisters broke out in my private parts, but I did not test positive for herpes. The visit and tests cost me a month's income.

This episode remained part of the mystery which I found too frustrating and far too expensive to research further. I didn't have health insurance since I'd resigned from my job as a teacher, and I wasn't earning much money, so I tried to make the best of it all on my own.

3. "Fine, thanks!"
acrylic and chalk pencil on birch
16" x 20", 2010

I also feared being a drag on friends and family by admitting how miserable I often felt. Cultural conditioning upheld my silence. "If you don't have something nice to say, don't say anything at all." "Keep a stiff upper lip." "Be self sufficient." "Keep trying harder." I tried so hard to be demure that it's no wonder people didn't notice when I "peeped". Their casual responses became an element in the vicious cycle of denial: as other people's minimization became internalized, I "normalized" my symptoms even as they were becoming more serious. I felt ashamed about complaining, thinking other people must be enduring the same conditions (but so much better than I) and that I was weak for making such suffering out of "normal" life. After all, everybody gets sore and stressed-out sometimes, and most parents of tiny tots are sleep-deprived.

What got me to "peep" louder was starting to learn how serious Lyme disease could become – not just some minor arthritis in the knees as I had once thought. Lyme is capable of producing a broad range of symptoms in different parts of the body. I read that if left untreated it could lead to brain lesions, organ failure, paralysis, dementia, and death. Some people who had been diagnosed as having severe anemia, leukemia, chronic fatigue syndrome, fibromyalgia, rheumatoid arthritis, lupus, MS (multiple sclerosis), Parkinson's, and ALS (amyotrophic lateral sclerosis; Lou Gehrig's disease) experienced significant improvement when their condition was found to include or even be caused by Lyme and other tick borne diseases and therefore was treatable through antibiotics. I also learned that symptoms of Lyme could wax and wane. I began to see how the seemingly unrelated symptoms I had endured on and off for many years could all be part of a larger picture.

The words on the dark side of this painting are from the paper *Advanced Topics In Lyme Disease: Diagnostic Hints And Treatment Guidelines For Lyme And Other Tick Borne Illnesses*, by Joseph J. Burrascano Jr., M.D. (2008). As I began to suspect that I had Lyme, I began talking with other people in my community who had it. They asked about my symptoms and then told me I was a "poster child" for it and to seek treatment immediately. The urge to cry out for help finally trumped my stoic silence and old fashioned "good manners."

4. Depression

Depression can be an illness onto itself, but it can also be a side effect of a physical illness. I fell into it several times a year for many years, but it always seemed to be in reaction to some condition beyond my control. Although tending to be a quiet, serious, and studious person, I didn't think of myself as a pessimistic or "depressed person" *per se*. During the good periods, I was perfectly capable of finding beauty and meaning in life. The pattern was that for a while I would feel creative, inspired, invested in my career, in love with my family, and perceive myself to be a well-adjusted, intelligent, and mature adult with a positive outlook on life. Then, unexpectedly, the bottom would drop out. I'd begin to feel lethargic, fatigued, unmotivated, sore, achy, arthritic, anxious, angry, spaced out, and stupid – not able to organize thoughts well or feel a sense of capability for carrying out the kinds of complex creative projects that made my life interesting. Inspiration and confidence would disintegrate, and I'd feel as if I'd fallen into a deep hole with no way out, or flipped over in a kayak that I couldn't right. There was only waiting – for weeks usually – before the sky would appear again. Then there was grief over lost time, a toll on my projects and relationships, and frustration about seeming to have so little control.

From 2001 to 2009 there was more falling and less rising as the cycles continued. The randomly occurring debilitating symptoms and lack of a sense of moving forward with my life on any front led to despondency and desperation. Twice during that period I sought medication for depression, but both times the person I consulted helped me conclude that I was a strong courageous woman with challenging life circumstances, but not clinically depressed.

This painting evolved from an idea to paint the form of a person in blue with an amorphous blue background. The first figure I rendered looked too cartoonish to symbolize depression, so I took a big brush and began swirling the wet paint into the background. Quickly a new figure emerged, a phantom from within the paint itself. I did a bit of work bringing it into completion, but the larger part of the composition lay in

4. Depression, acrylic on art board, 20" x 16", 2009

5. Rock Bottom, acrylic and sand on art board, 20" x 16", 2009

recognizing what had spontaneously emerged beyond my conscious efforts – and letting it be. Herein lies a lesson from the experience of being ill: it's simply a fact that I can't control as much as I thought I could, and what I can control is on the inside more than the outside. Much of "what works out" does so because I've opened up to seeing it in a different way, not because I've understood how to make it work better through my willful efforts. A positive side effect of being so ill for so long is that it caused me to consider new ways of viewing myself. Who is the "me" who thinks she has to have control? What observes, unperturbed, even as "I" appear to be suffering? In spite of physical setbacks there can still be soulful progress. The figure in the painting seems to be alone and suffering, yet she is floating and surrounded by light.

5. Rock Bottom

Rock Bottom was the first image that came to mind to paint, giving form to the formless experience of fatigue and having "bottomed out" in so many ways. For years I looked outward and blamed life's circumstances for inducing symptoms of stress and fatigue – divorce, returning to full time work, remarriage, pregnancy, separation, unmedicated birth of a 10 lb. 14 oz. baby, nursing around the clock, a second divorce, home-schooling two highly creative children, moving four times in six years, job loss, financial strain.

I also blamed myself, thinking if only I could learn to deal with stress better and have a more positive attitude, then I'd feel better. Gradually, in spite of my best efforts, things just kept falling apart – not only my career, intimate relationships, and family connectedness, but also my inner life. What I clung to as foundational beliefs kept failing to make life feel better. Whenever I adopted a new spiritual or philosophical mindset to help me interpret what was going on and navigate through it, it might have some useful effect for a little while, but ultimately could not hold me together through the next phase of debilitating symptoms. The bottom just kept falling out.

While it is true that life's circumstances were a source of stress, the other hidden side of the circle was that a physical disease was strongly influencing every aspect of my life. I noticed friends and neighbors encountering births, deaths, job changes, and divorces – going through stressful periods – but having the physical stamina and internal coherence to manage these changes and go on with their lives in a vibrant way. In comparison, I felt like a person riding a bicycle on the shoulder of the freeway. Eventually I became so ill that there was no capacity left for "trying harder" to "make things work" anymore. That was the turning point.

Although the idea of falling can have negative connotations – giving up, failure, loss of control, disgrace – it can also be about surrender, letting go of resistance. The experience of bottoming out can be full of grace and positive potential. There is relief in having landed. One has finished for now. Dying? Waiting? Who knows what is to come? There is rest, at last. Perhaps that is the only choice any more, so it is finally allowed to happen. There is relief in total surrender.

Perhaps the figure in the rock/egg is gestating, going through metamorphosis. To signify that the scene was under water I sprinkled sand onto the wet paint and added a few strokes of green to the upper left as if light were shining through it. Adding a touch of this green to the top of the figure revealed the idea to me (I didn't know it going in) that, although she appeared to be alone, there was a healing presence – green light or energy – reaching her through the dark water. Thus was the title for the exhibit conceived.

6. One Step at a Time

In late April 2009, after visiting relatives in the Berkshires, I noticed a little pink dot above my ankle which expanded into a two inch wide red circle with a bruised, blistery center. It didn't hurt, but itched enough to make me notice. That was the first clue. It looked like a bull's eye to me. I went back to my doctor. She didn't think it was a Lyme rash because of the bruise and the fact that it itched, but she sent out a blood test to see. Next clue: at the library I saw a book on the "new book table" titled *Cure Unknown: Inside the Lyme Epidemic*, by Pamela Weintraub. I hadn't gone to the library consciously seeking

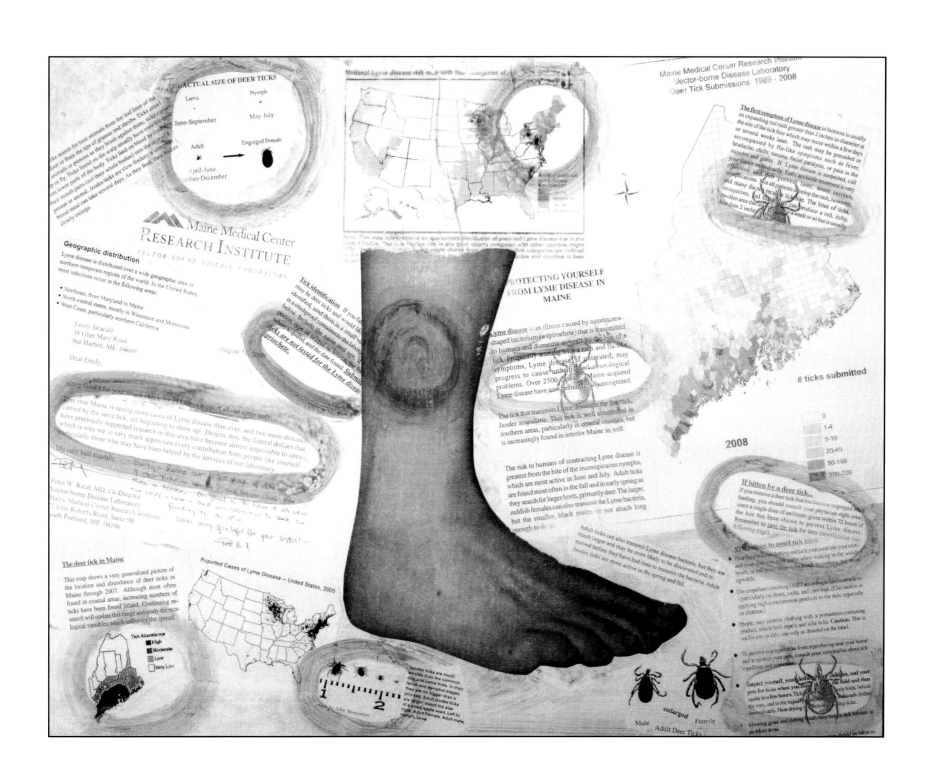

6. One Step at a Time
acrylic and paper collage on birch
16" x 20", 2010

information about Lyme disease (believing I already knew what it was and wasn't), nor had I possessed the focus or stamina to read adult nonfiction books for a long while, but I felt strongly drawn to check out the book. Pouring through it over the next 36 hours was a revelatory experience. The more I read, the more I made the connection between the stories of people with *chronic* Lyme and my own symptoms going back for many years.

Although (as it turns out) I have always lived in potentially tick-infested areas and have spent much time lingering in nature, such as painting scenic views, I never used to know to check for ticks. I also had no idea how large (or small) they could be. Memories began to resurface of times I thought I had gotten a splinter somehow – times when I had picked and poked at a tiny black dot, trying in vain to squeeze it out. From having gardened, I made the association between that kind of splinter which is embedded straight in and looks like a pinpoint, and times when I'd gotten a rose briar or thorn stuck in my leg. Now I believe those "splinters" were really embedded ticks. Instead of a one-shot deal, I saw myself as having had multiple exposures over many years. I also learned there could be no rash at all, or other (non-bull's eye) rashes from the other tick borne diseases, even years later.

Over the next month I became sicker and sicker, but in all the same ways that I had felt on and off for years. It was frightening enough to keep my attention focused and help me do things out of character such as pestering the front desk at the clinic with one message after another, asking if the test were back (it was negative), asking for another test (also negative), explaining in a letter that this was typical for long-term cases, writing and hand delivering an eight page letter about my symptoms, getting a referral to another doctor, and asking to start antibiotics while waiting for the first appointment. I felt my health declining back into the craziest of prior low points. My spine felt electric and "buzzy" inside. There was so much swelling in my joints and tail bone area that it limited my natural stride. Walking two blocks to the library and back left me flat and exhausted for the rest of the day. I had a relentless pressure headache, dizziness, tipsiness like being drunk,

trouble judging distances, and I frequently tripped on the stairs in my small house. I narrowly avoided three car accidents from overlooking the approach of other cars while trying to drive across streets in my small town neighborhood. My bones and muscles ached like an acute case of the flu. Holding a telephone up to my ear for a three minute conversation felt like holding a difficult yoga pose that burned. I was short of breath and felt like crying all the time.

The appointment with the Lyme Aware doctor kept getting moved back for various necessary reasons until the first week in July. During May and June, the round rash slowly receded until all that was left was a bruise. (One year later it was still visible and tender.) During those two months I began to wake up from my own denial and to assemble facts and figures to get other people's attention. It was exasperating yet empowering. It got me to stand up for myself more than I ever had before.

7. Fluff and Icebergs

Coming out of denial and into acknowledgement of my body's condition was a back and forth process. Before I got the validation of a doctor's diagnosis, I wavered between worrying I was making up a story – taking it all too seriously – and then feeling certain that I needed medical help immediately, but worrying that no one would believe that unless I made a big deal about it myself. I had to begin by taking my own needs seriously instead of trying to ignore them.

Looking back, there were intuitive hints for years: there were dreams of trying to pull some kind of sickening white stuff out of my mouth – it just kept coming and coming; I needed to get it out of my body. There were many dreams of becoming too crippled to walk, my feet not having any power or coordination.

The moment I finally landed into full body "knowing" that my body was truly very sick had nothing to do with a formal medical event. It was after telling one of my very intuitive friends about what I thought *might* be happening. "What can I do to help?", she asked. That's when I knew. Something

7. Fluff and Icebergs,
acrylic and cotton on birch
16" x 20", 2010

undeniable slipped into place. It was a feeling of deep acknowledgement, of resonance, of coming into focus. I no longer felt foolish or confused. At last I surrendered to being honest with myself, come what may.

My friend gave me Reiki treatments once a week for several months. In one session, before I shared my "white fluff" dreams, she had a vision that she was pulling some kind of white "stuffing" out of my abdomen. Another time she shared a vision of icebergs melting, and as they were melting I was getting better. I took that as a positive sign. My immune system was not functioning well, and I felt cold all the time. 96.4 was my "normal"; 98.6 felt like a running a fever, with sweating and an erratically racing heart. The image of melting ice also connected with the idea that my "life force" had been "stuck in deep freeze" for a long time. Now that I've gotten back into painting and writing it feels as if this frozen potential is flowing again. After many years of feeling stuck and confused, I'm now finding it easier than ever to sense and trust intuitive guidance and then act accordingly.

8. Permanent Records

This piece began as a charcoal sketch done in Jungian therapy in early 2009, before I knew about Lyme. Starting therapy that January was my first attempt in many years to reach out for help in searching for answers and to confide about my private storms. This sketch depicted the disintegration of so many of the "official" aspects of my identity. Some papers represented certificates of special career training and diplomas that had once seemed important, but now seemed to make no difference in my ability to make a living, advance along a career path, or experience well-being – they had become mere slips of paper. Other papers represented legal documents and contracts: all my former jobs, an expired teaching license, two marriage licenses, two sets of divorce papers. It seemed as if most of what used to define "me" had been "blown away."

Soon after sketching this piece I began to learn about Lyme disease and to identify with anecdotes about other people's experiences of it. This inspired me to search through boxes of

my old journals (there was a closet-full). There I discovered descriptions bearing witness to this illness and its effects. It was amazing to have a whole new lens through which to view past struggles. The new "Lyme colored lens" put such a different spin on everything.

This process of review and revision helped me begin to release a cache of long hidden guilt, anger, shame, frustration, and resentment. Assembling sections from those journals suddenly became a compelling project. Finally I began to connect the dots of all aspects of my experience, inner and outer, and to acknowledge the body's need for more attention and support.

Those notes, describing changes in my health and abilities, became the foundation for three hours' worth of health history interviews with my new doctor. Having these details in writing was essential for me because within the flow of a spoken dialogue I was often unable to recall important facts or to speak articulately. I would stammer nervously, lose my train of thought, and sweat profusely when trying to focus and give clear answers. I was what is informally called "a mess."

Later that year, as leaves began to fall, I felt drawn to release the past symbolically by burning much of my old writing. The empty clip on this painting is an artifact from that purge. Suspended from it hang three pages of journal entries from four months in 2002. They describe the dramatic fluctuations between sickness and health that can be common with chronic Lyme disease and its attendant co-infections.

Lyme Log from Journals

8-6-02 "This a.m. my head and body ache. ...Looking back [on the past school year and setting intentions for more self care in upcoming year when I would teach grades 3-4] I now realize what I accepted as a "normal" day included awakening panic stricken, having to pray in order to get out of bed, dreading the day ahead, not knowing what to feed myself, not wanting to feed myself, putting on a good face and clothes – hard, because I didn't know what to wear nor want to go out into public, exhausted, wrung out, sore all over, fragile, easily

8. Permanent Records
charcoal, acrylic, paper, string, and metal on art board
16" x 20", 2009

enraged or moved to tears. Little appetite nor centeredness to tune in about my needs. Came to tears or other strong emotions on a daily basis, and frequently had a hard time thinking quickly. Frequent colds and sore throats. Hard time sleeping, frequent anxiety attacks on personal time."

8-14-02 "Why does the bottom keep dropping out? Between 10 pm when I lay down, and 11 pm, I went from fully focused, positive, confident, relaxed, to feeling psychologically hazed, deranged, caught off-guard, like I was living a nightmare. That's the typical pattern. I can't figure out how it falls apart, what my part is..."

[undated, middle of August] "Hot flashes, aching body and heart, tears... Many moments I almost feel I could capsize, but I keep going. ...My conception of TIME changes radically from hour to hour...hundreds of times today I felt like giving up. Some glandular swelling, some toxic release left..."

[undated, end of August] "Restful sleep, peaceful and calm awakening, inner harmony, sweet gladness about the day, the future, seeing with heart open. I feel more balanced, centered and whole than almost ever in recent memory. I feel more settled and stable than in a long time, and that it is really who I am. I do not believe I am manic-depressive. I believe I have been living with intense inner change, also grief. I have been sad. These days are so bright. Since Tuesday I've felt like I've been in a new life - good vibes, inner strength. I'm excited about school starting."

9-6-02 "Things went very well at school this week in my class. It is alive - I love having a bigger class. LOTS of joy!!!"

9-12-02 "...angry and cried uncontrollably, so upset at recess that I couldn't stand it and cried. Blurry boundaries - I feel all worn out and mixed up. Period." "I don't feel strong and confident. Back to feeling very vulnerable and childlike and like I can't maintain a sensation inside of being grown up. Weary. Where is my health? Feels like my whole body is aching, shoulders and neck and face - all stiff and yucky, joints sore. I feel contaminated. I don't know where the feelings of being enthusiastic and positive and mature went to. It feels like

being a different person. I feel like I'm dreaming. I feel very introverted. I am disgusted by these fluctuations and exhausted by trying to be certain ways. I feel like my life is so messed up, it's hard to know what to do. Clarity disintegrates so quickly. I forget who I am so easily. I feel numb and sore and exhausted. Can't find perspective through mental effort. Can't make myself be happy or content. I feel confused - strained mentally, emotionally, physically." "Nothing is making sense. It all seems random and I have no enthusiasm or conviction. It feels like I'm in a dream and I can't wake up and no one is coming to help - it all seems senseless."

9-20-02 [nice printing again] "Another delicious week of hard work and enjoying it, at school. I am glad to work there. I am glad to be that role. Living abundantly, counting blessings. Flowing into Friday again, a quick week. Living deeply each day, connected, full, but not too much... Relishing life. Appetite for food and life."

10-2-02 "Head buzzing. I have a hard time letting go of mental control mode - like getting stuck in the "on" position. No emotions, frozen. Not caring to be with others or do things for pleasure. Overwhelmed. I feel like there's a thick dark wall between me and the world, like my eyes can't see the colors."

10-3-02 "I'm sad and mad and exhausted and unhinged. ...I feel I am in a world in the fog, in my own universe."

10-4-02 "A lot of energy in my pelvis and R hip joint and heart. Right now I feel warm, relaxed, present. Coming out of almost a week of feeling unbalanced, anxious, tense, afraid, worried, blustery, angry, sad, confused. My moods were so strong and charged so much this week and I went in and out so quickly. I am getting bored with my own stories, how things are always so complex and on the edge and up for questioning and uncertain and complicated with contorted conflicts. It would be a blessing to go on in a much simpler way... to not be delusional and lost in the nightmare quality of life... The forces affecting my moods and perceptions feel enormous. I have no way to control or challenge them mentally. I can only keep surrendering."

10-8-02 "Tuesday. Disconnected to past – unhinged. Paintings, memories of teaching... I seem to be standing on the outside looking in, estranged from life flow. Disconcerting – can't find warmth in the present. Sub-level not surface-level emotions. Like a radio on inside but can't hear it on the outside."

10-9-02 [after massage] "Feeling more calm and relaxed than in a long time... I feel very glad and excited to be teaching again."

10-11-02 "Will I ever stop feeling like I'm going insane, periodically? Will it get worse? I am terrified of flaking out. Will I ever learn to manage my stress better? Will I feel more emotionally stable? Are things as crazy as they seem? I am so tired. I am tired and I want to go home."

Friday [no date] "More possible chicken pox. [Several students in my class have chicken pox] Enjoying sleep (when I can — still up at 2:30, hard to go under again.) Actually everything seems to have a dreamlike quality, as if my senses and feelings were muted."

10-12-02 "Weird perceptions. Chicken pox [or shingles or other unknown rash] emerging, little "fly bites" itchy. Arthritis ache in right arm. Noises loud, can't understand how I got here. Sensitive all over. I am sick. Outgassing poisons through the skin. It feels like I'm in a dream, nothing is clear. It feels like someone else did those paintings. I can't find myself – the self who can do that. I feel lost to myself and not sure how to get back or go forward. I'm sick and tired of running into one rut after another. How the hell am I supposed to trust ANYTHING if the things I feel deeply don't last? I give up. I'm done. Take me home. I withdraw from this course..."

10-14-02 "Also I am aware that even when I am "out of sorts" lately, it is small turbulence compared to a year ago. I feel more present and centered than in a long time."

10-18-02 "Itchy skin, It feels like I'm stuck inside a nightmare and I can't wake up. People not taking it seriously when I say I'm sick or exhausted. I want to quit."

Wed. [no date] "Every day different, very much. Contemplating leaving the school mid year if possible...last night I put great willpower into calming my body... Feeling strong, looking forward to next month of school." "Considerations: making transition out of this school. I have felt much anger and disgust and antipathy this month and heard myself saying same words as in marriage: 'I can't take this anymore, I want out.' Yet also slowing down and considering how I could do this departure differently. I really do love the children and the work."

10-25-02 "Tired irritated worn out disgusted, more rash – maybe shingles. I've Had it up to Here! Mtgs NON STOP 8-5 This is unsustainable."

10-29-02 Wed. "Intense headaches, some nausea ~ not cresting. Body not happy but soul and heart ~ intense week."

11-1-02 "It couldn't get much hotter than this. So much shit, my body is almost convulsing. Tail bone hurts, gut, neck, throat. I'm in deep heavy labor. Sore all over, emotionally as sore as can be. It is all coming to a head. I can't take any more intensity without exploding. Up until midnight 3 days in a row now. I hurt all over. I hurt so bad it feels like I'm being ripped apart or going to explode."

11-2-02 "This is really intense but I'm getting through it. After two days of hell, I am now more complete, stable, grounded. A lot of pressure in tail bone area."

11-5-02 "My pelvis aches."

"Sat. a.m. [no date] the tide has turned. Uplift! From grayest gloomy mood irritable, grouchy, to hopefulness and RELIEF!"

"Sun. a.m. [no date] I feel almost too tired to do anything. Fatigue radiating out of [picture of thymus gland on chest]. Thymus gland, heart area feels very strained. Like when you lose your breath and strain for air. I have another sore throat and sinus infection. I feel very vulnerable. I also feel relieved of the effort of trying to control. Letting go of the classroom and parent teacher conferences is one more huge release...my heart pulled me through this...I want to be all

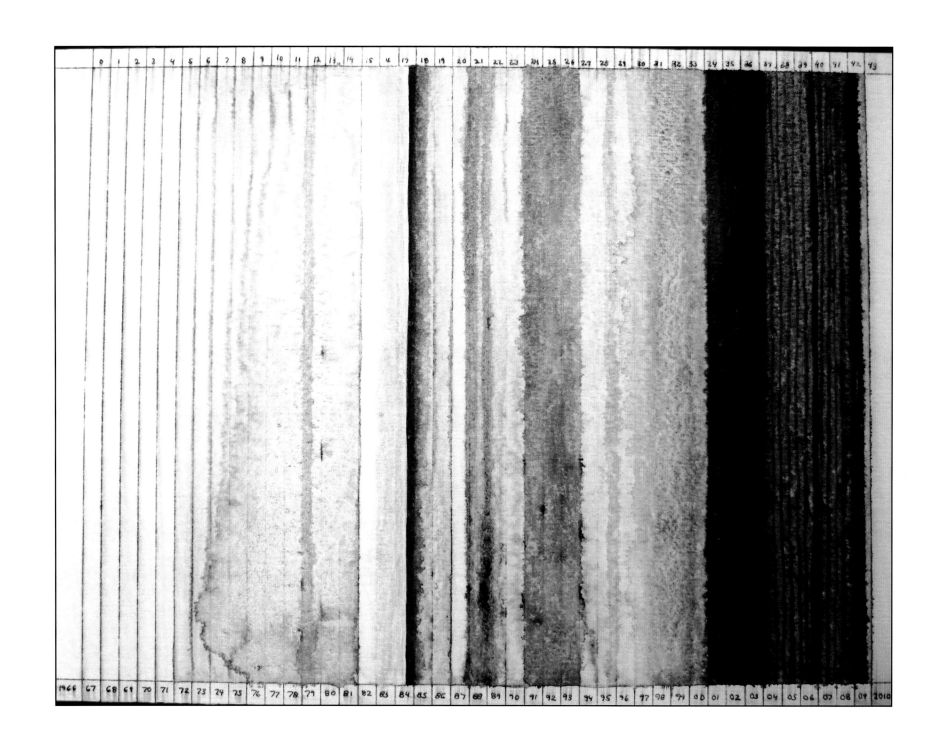

9. Bar Code
acrylic and pen on art board
16" x 20", 2010

that I can be. I want to feel deeply fulfilled I want to wake up to the divine in daily life and not go back to sleep."

11-25-02 "Palpable stability coming in, up through my feet. Patchy fog, clearing."

"Day after Thanksgiving. [no date] Mind feels like scrambled eggs. No certainty."

9. Bar Code

For people who have had Lyme disease for a long time before starting treatment, it is not unusual to get a negative blood test. The blood tests are not perfect. For one thing, the blood stream is not the bacterium's favorite place to hang out, more of a transportation network it rides through to get to other places. Nor does it have to rely on that method. In its spirochete form, *Bb* can literally drill itself through bodily tissues and individual cell walls. The bacteria can live inside our cells, even white blood cells, like the proverbial "wolf in sheep's clothing", cloaking themselves in the cells' membranes, thereby stealthily disguising themselves from our own immune system's detection. Current Lyme tests do not assess all strains of *Bb* –which continues to evolve. Antibodies the test assesses may not be present in detectable levels if the test is done too soon after a tick bite. Even more appalling, if the patient's body has a raging case of Lyme there may not be a detectable level of antibodies in the blood because they are all in use, bound to the bacteria! Taking anti-inflammatory steroidal drugs can suppress one's immune system, reducing an antibody response. If Lyme tests come back negative, patients and doctors should also be thinking of testing for other tick borne diseases which cause some symptoms identical to Lyme but would obviously not turn up on a Lyme blood test.

In the absence of a positive blood test as proof of having Lyme disease, I put together an extensive written health history from memories and journal entries to describe my "normal" health and abilities, how they changed, and when. This not only provided clues to what the illness might be, it also turned up even more of an ants' nest.

The descent into the cavern I was currently in (2009) began in 2001, but during three hours of intense interviewing my Lyme-savvy doctor identified a probable "meeting with a tick" in 1984 when I was still in high school, and theorized that I might have been exposed much earlier in childhood. (I grew up in rural Northern Michigan, with dairy goats, and deer in the woods and fields, and spent much of my free time playing and painting outside. Frequent respiratory and digestive ailments, fatigue, splitting headaches, and severely aching knees, legs, and ankles go back to early grade school. This was diagnosed as "allergies" for which I got weekly shots and "growing pains" for which I wore special orthopedic shoes to raise my arches.)

The possibility of having had Lyme changed my self perception and put new interpretations on much of my life story. "Amazing" is how I put it. "Coming out of denial" is how my doctor put it. Low energy, achy joints, swollen glands, loud popping sounds in the neck? "Normal" for this body. Other conditions I had thought were "normal", such as having to pee every hour or two turned out not to be; it's just that I'd been living with them for over half my life.

Curious to examine this history visually, I drew a column for each year of my life. As I began darkening patches to represent degrees of illness, I could see patterns forming; not only on the paper – a bar code sort of thing – but also in terms of significant choices. I began to see how being sick in a Lyme-ish sort of way had affected choices I'd made in my personal, social, educational, professional, and recreational life; based on my energy level, cognitive clarity, and emotional stability – or the lack thereof.

10. Mad Math

This visual aid was inspired by the anti-drug campaign from the 1980s: your brain as an egg, a fried egg as "your brain on drugs." In recent years I often described my brain as feeling like "scrambled eggs" during those flipped-over-kayak times. My thoughts could easily get scrambled as well. When I imagined illustrating this, the idea of tangled yarn arose as a non-culinary alternative. Crocheting the healthy brain was a fun

10. Mad Math
acrylic, yarn, paper, metal, and foam board on birch
16" x 20", 2010

and healing experience; quite a "brain gym" workout as I stretched my concentration to 1) figure out how to make a brain from yarn in the first place, and 2) duplicate the hemispheres with some semblance of symmetry. The spiraled strands of yarn on the disc in the middle are supposed to be an enlarged view of the Lyme bacteria, a spirochete form. Anyone familiar with them may shudder at the close resemblance!

The background for the healthy brain is a piece of music I used to play at the Interlochen Arts Academy, an international school for the arts where I went to high school. In eleventh grade I was among the top students in the clarinet section. I was also a kid who liked to take standardized tests and typically came out several years above grade. That year, 1984, I was awarded the Rensselaer medal for Math and Science, along with a summer scholarship to the Rensselaer Polytechnic Institute as the top math and science student in the junior class. Instead, I chose to attend the Bennington July Program in southern Vermont and take classes in clarinet technique, music composition, and plant-based medicinal chemistry. The rural Green Mountain scenery was a big draw. I loved to sit in the fields – writing, painting, thinking. I flourished in all my classes, and with faculty encouragement applied for early admission to the college. After joining my family for a vacation through scenic places down the East Coast from Mount Desert Island to Manhattan, I came home to discover that I had been accepted to Bennington for the fall. My plan was to double-major in Pre-Med and music composition.

Then, in August, I came down with what felt like a case of the flu, with a high fever, aches and pains, no vomiting, but generally feeling very sick all over. Flu in the summer seemed unusual, but then we had just come back from traveling so it seemed reasonable to have been exposed to some germs I was not used to. Now I know that flu symptoms in summer is a reason to suspect Lyme or other tick borne diseases.

The acute illness seemed to resolve itself (the fever dropped), except that by the end of the month I also felt as if my brain were being "rewired." It was a visceral, electrical sensation, with mental and emotional ramifications. For several reasons I

decided to finish high school at Interlochen, much closer to home. In my journals from senior year the handwriting changes radically from the previously steady script of springtime. I describe trembling hands and intense energy in my spine as well as unshakable fatigue and roving aches and pains. I describe feeling uncharacteristically paranoid, anxious, tearful, depressed, hypersensitive, and mentally overwhelmed by jumbled thoughts, unable to focus without sheer effort. These episodes are contrasted by periods of feeling emotionally blank, numbed out, disoriented, in "another world," as if I am floating, dissociated from everything, as if my mind were "too smooth and hard for any new fact to penetrate and stick." I wrote of being afraid of going insane, wishing to just drop out of school and go live in a simple mountain retreat away from everything. (And I never got drunk or did hallucinogenic drugs. Really.)

Reading text and music became a strain. I had already demonstrated a tendency toward dyslexia under pressure, but until that year I had thought of myself as a smart, confident, dedicated, and very capable student. Following lectures became ever more difficult. Complex analysis of ideas under pressure, such as during essay exams, and committing new facts to memory became very difficult. I couldn't remember things well nor learn quickly anymore; it all became a huge effort. Instead of my usual two to three hours of practicing clarinet every day, I would often sit in the practice room zoning out, with the instrument on my lap, staring at the wall. I couldn't seem to focus on the notes and got winded easily. At the beginning of the school year I still had the technical prowess to be a contender for an upper seat in the orchestra, but by the end of the year I had fallen to second from the bottom of the clarinet section in the concert band. Being in music ensembles felt awful – the noise made me dizzy. I often felt out of breath, but blamed this, as well as the atrophy of other technical abilities, on my lack of practice. I couldn't understand why I seemed to be slipping in all subjects.

For some reason I didn't consider myself an innocent victim of illness. I still assessed my self worth in terms of outer performance. I felt frustrated, embarrassed, awkward, and

11. Strength as Weakness
acrylic and pencil on art board
16" x 20", 2010

most of all guilty, as if I were failing to "get my act together," and therefore I tried to hide the problems even more. Some people thought I just had an attitude problem; a condition called "Senioritis." It became apparent to my (new that year) clarinet teacher that doing the required Senior Recital would be impossible for me, so I played one simple duet in another girl's recital instead.

The next fall I started college at Amherst, found the academic pace very daunting, and felt stressed out and under the weather most of the time. Mid sophomore year I transferred to College of the Atlantic where the class size was much smaller, I had more one-on-one help from teachers, and was able to do more self-directed projects at my own pace. I never returned to the formal study of music, took only one required science class in college (squeaked by with a passing grade), and somehow managed to never take a college level math class! I don't know if there are really any lesions in my brain, but working with numbers (even adding simple numbers) still doesn't come easily, and I often make mistakes even when I try not to.

11. Strength as Weakness

How did these changes in ability not raise eyebrows? For one thing, most people close to me already knew I loved the humanities and visual arts as much as music, math, and science, so the switch to art, religion, and philosophy courses at Amherst, and then to philosophy and education at COA were still within my "profile of interest." Also, since I didn't believe that taking a "time out" to collapse was possible, I just kept using whichever abilities worked better. While memorizing and recalling data and facts became more difficult, pondering philosophical thoughts and writing my own ideas still came relatively easily. Perfectionism and pride as much as patience drove me to spend as much time and effort as necessary to complete assignments, so my grades remained "fine." No longer a straight A student, but still looking "normal" with all passing grades, it was frustrating to try so hard but not excel.

Mentally and physically my health did improve somewhat after high school. If I did have Lyme back then, it may have been tamped down by frequent use of antibiotics for other ailments such as sinus infections. It was easy to get antibiotics. When I was a child my mother could even call the doctor, describe my symptoms, and get a prescription filled for my dad to pick up on his way home from work! However, by the time I became a parent in 1995, at age 28, most pediatricians counseled that it was wiser to try everything else before going the route of antibiotics – and I agreed. This change in climate of opinion set the tone for my refraining from seeking a doctor's help or medication to help with my symptoms later on; I was used to making the best of what I was going through on my own. I saw allopathic medicine as a last resort.

Looking back I recalled other episodes of illness in my 20s and 30s that might have been Lyme related: summer fevers with internally originating aches, pains, and fatigue (not due to any obvious overactivity such as sports). Sleeping and resting didn't make them go away. There were mysterious periods of searing pain in the torso. Once it was so severe that I went to the ER suspecting a heart attack, but no cause appeared. "Probably a virus." "It must be a virus" was code for "there's nothing we can do for you," so when these pains came back I just endured them. Sometimes I could hardly move or breathe, the pains were so sharp. To stand up I'd have to roll over and crawl out of bed. I wondered how I could have strained and injured myself in my sleep. There were muscle aches and joint aches to the point where I'd be limping, but I always had some explanation: it was the bicycle ride, gardening, climbing stairs with laundry from the basement, getting out of bed without "limbering up" first. I was often very tired and "under the weather," but was able to push through it and keep working.

I used to believe that focusing outward and doing what was asked of me to the best of my ability was the definition of "acting responsibly." Eventually all this pushing and ignoring led to a robotic relationship to my work and other people. "Getting the job done" eclipsed a felt sense of connection with myself and other people. Now I am aware that I'm responsible for looking within and being honest with myself about what is going on inside as well. Sometimes that means asking for help. I'm discovering true strength can sometimes feel very soft.

12. Half an Apple
acrylic on art board
16" x 20", 2009

12. Half an Apple

After college and a year and a half of international travel, I worked as a grade school teacher, moonlighting as a private art teacher and artist. My ability to concentrate and speak articulately was high enough to successfully manage complex jobs such as teaching in a one-room school with 13 students (all grades, all subjects) and teaching K-8 art to 550 students a week (all of whom I knew by name and connected with as individuals), but I always felt the need to ramp up into a hyper-vigilant state of being "on edge" because it took great effort to focus, remember, speak, and lead coherently. I most enjoyed teaching small adult art classes such as Creativity Recovery Workshops at home. Most mornings in my 20s I woke up feeling tired and achy, but I adored my students and felt successful, even if teaching took all the effort I could muster.

As with college, it seemed to me as if most other young adults around me had much more energy to spend in their off hours. While friends, peers, and colleagues went out on the town, ran marathons, backpacked through mountains, and sought advanced degrees, I took only the minimum required "professional development" workshops and preferred to spend my limited free time quietly painting, writing, and reading on my own. Pregnancy and the birth of my daughter at the end of my 20s was a great excuse to take a time-out from formal education and formal employment. I was able to be a full time parent in a supportive community. My husband at the time was in graduate school, so we lived in family housing. I could have kept my teaching license intact by taking just one class, but that was out of the question, energy-wise. I couldn't understand how so many of my friends managed to attend college as well as raise their children! I was so grateful to be able to just hang out with my toddler at the sandbox. Living gently, in harmony with my child's needs for frequent little meals and rest times, as well as lots of time sitting together painting and reading picture books, I got through well enough.

Between 2001 and 2003 everything started to fall apart again. I was newly divorced, teaching art and grades 2-4 at a private school. Lyme seems to thrive in a body that is already under stress. For a few days at a time I would feel like a capable adult: Classroom Teacher, Student-Teacher Supervisor of a college level education student who worked in my class, Faculty Chair, Board Member, Single Working Mom. Then, for no apparent reason, I would slip into an internal sensation of profound anxiety and confusion which I defined at the time as an irrational regression into "immaturity." I also described (only in my journals) feeling like a two dimensional "paper" person. Sometimes I felt as if I were physically floating in the air. Sometimes my legs ached so badly I had to drag myself up the stairs by the railing. Although I had so many other physical symptoms as well – a stiff neck, weird electrical sensations in my head and limbs, roving aches, odd rashes, and swelling in the joints – I viewed them each as a separate issue and chalked them up to "stress", "inevitable middle-age aches and pains", and "an allergy to poison ivy" (which I seemed to mysteriously be getting rashes from even though I knew to avoid the plants; I figured the dog or other household members might have gotten into it and somehow gotten it on me.)

As in high school, I focused on appearing competent, hiding my symptoms, and interpreting my problems as signs of personal weakness. Unknown to me at the time, several students in the school and a colleague of mine came down with Lyme disease, and all of them believed their exposure was on our school grounds, a forest with many deer. (Some were first diagnosed with arthritis, fibromyalgia, chronic fatigue, depression, anxiety, and difficulty learning to read, before their true illness was determined and effectively treated.)

This painting portrays how I felt when teaching under the influence of a neurological state commonly described by Lyme patients as "brain fog," symbolized in the painting as an approaching bank of fog. The teacher is represented as a stick figure a child might draw. Although she is made up to be as "perfect" as can be in her color-coordinated outfit, students are beginning to suspect that she is "not all there." Like the numbers on the board there is still a degree of sensibility and order, but how it is being delivered is starting to seem somewhat floaty and tipsy. Teaching Waldorf grade-school curriculum involves much oral story telling and reciting of

"Don't you remember, we talked about that yesterday? Really, you don't? I asked you to you please remember to check the names of those and add the list we talked about, which I'll leave

I'm sorry. I don't remember.
I'm sorry. I don't remember...
I'm sorry. I don't remember...
I'm sorry. I don't remember...
I'm sorry. I don't

13. Remember?
acrylic on art board
16" x 20", 2009

memorized verses and facts. Memorizing anything was futile for me, so I often felt as if I was faking my way as a Waldorf teacher by using cue cards. I played up my strengths, such as organizing the room nicely so that anyone who entered saw orderliness and beauty. Since visual art is one of my strengths I could still lead my class in illustrating their "main lesson books" and creating beautiful paintings for the walls.

In spring 2002, I declined the renewal of my contract for the coming school year. Over the summer my health stabilized just enough so that I reapplied for my old position and was re-hired, but by November I became too ill to teach and resigned. It seems hard to believe now, but at the time it didn't occur to me to share with anyone the health difficulties I was facing. I was still operating from the belief that I had somehow failed to maintain good health and was guilty of giving up; I'd failed to marshal the strength and balance to overcome my difficulties. Nor did it occur to me to apply for disability. I thought that was for people with a permanent impairment such as blindness. Without a job, I no longer had health insurance nor income to pay for expensive checkups out-of-pocket, so I didn't go to a doctor. Instead, I tried to treat some symptoms on my own with health-food store items such as salves, flower essences, herbal tinctures, and homeopathic remedies. I knew Reiki and other hands-on healing techniques that I could exchange with other practitioners for free, and I bartered with a friend for Integrated Awareness sessions. While these holistic approaches did help soothe me somewhat, I continued to go through ups and downs, and overall there was the feeling of an undertow pulling me into deeper waters.

Looking back with more information, I now believe that the "brain fog" was most likely encephalitis and meningitis – inflammation of the brain and membranes around the brain and spinal cord – a state beyond my ability to control any more than the teacher and class can control the weather outside their windows.

In this painting it was fun to mix different levels of abstraction and realism, including a perspective that is somewhat skewed and half an apple going brown. Another visual pun in this

painting is that the three planes of the room converge behind the teacher. I did that on purpose to put the visual emphasis on her, but later realized that she is literally "in the zone of the vanishing point." Another joke, which I did intend, is that everyone has an eraser. Waldorf students are not usually given erasers (to promote best effort and concentration the first time around and avoid obsessive erasing and trying over). I gave everyone an eraser so that whatever was done could be undone if necessary; a positive spin on the idea of forgetting and an allusion to recovery.

13. Remember?

When looking for fonts to print this dialogue I stumbled across "School House Printed" and was tickled by the connotation of a school kid writing on the chalk board as a punishment. This explicit reference to "being guilty" made me laugh and confront the idea with humor: Was I really *trying* to be a space cadet? No. I made this painting soon after starting antibiotics in the summer of 2009. I was just beginning to realize that much of my short and long term memory loss could be given a new explanation that left all parties blameless. I used to think of myself as a "sharp" competent person, but more and more I felt frustrated about forgetting things – particularly verbal requests. "In one ear and out the other" had become the usual way of it.

As the situation worsened between 2001 and 2009, I lost all confidence to work outside my home except for a little independent house cleaning and light gardening, both of which sapped all my energy, but both could be done privately – little human interaction was needed, nor was reading or writing or math. I often felt childlike or simple-minded among other adults. I had difficulty following step by step instructions, such as how to program the sprinkler system at the nursery where I watered plants. For this reason I would not recommend therapies that include much verbal instruction and listening until a Lyme patient has gone through other preliminary treatment to deal with detoxing the brain. It may be impossible to string together more than two ideas in a row and maintain a logical connection, much less reflect upon those ideas and respond verbally or follow through on movement activities that

14. Brain Fog
acrylic and tulle on art board
16" x 20", 2010

are guided. Functionally, the experience of being inebriated is not far from the mark.

One might think that taking notes would help, but trying to mentally switch gears between listening and writing was as difficult as trying to translate words into another language. I usually blamed these listening comprehension and memory problems on being stressed out and preoccupied.

At home I did some illustration work and enjoyed teaching private art classes to small groups of adults and children around my dining room table, but eventually teaching just one class per day became too exhausting. By 2008 I started to mix up students' names. Talking to their parents after class during pick-up felt halting and awkward. Facilitating discussions with members of the adult group was exhausting. I could not continue even these intimate home-based classes. It was as if I were on autopilot all the time. I just wanted to be alone and space out and rest. I stopped teaching and began passing on my vast collection of art supplies to other art teachers and home-schooling parents – folding up camp. The one benefit of earning so little and spending all of my savings to make ends meet was that I finally qualified for basic subsidized state health insurance. But I still didn't go to a doctor. I still took my challenges personally, as if I were to blame for being weak. I would also look outward and blame my single- parent/head-of-household/low-income status for the stress. There seemed to be no way out of that tangled mess.

Word finding was another challenge which affected my ability to engage in ordinary dialogue. My daughter got used to finishing my sentences:

> "Honey, can you... um,...get me...that...um,...thing...?"
> "Your cup of tea?"
> "Yes, thanks!"

My verbal interactions with people were often "brittle" and short. Even in casual conversations, such as with drive-through tellers at the bank and clerks at the grocery store I would often get stuck trying to remember simple words and fumble mid-

sentence, so eventually I stopped trying. Any outings into the world – the library, the bank, and the grocery store (that's what it was down to) – were an enormous challenge. I would use breathing to control my high anxiety and just try to get the chores done and return home as quickly as possible.

I was mostly out of visiting contact with all but two of my friends, and rarely spoke on the phone with relatives (who all lived out of state), but this did not stand out since all of us still corresponded via e-mail. Actual conversation required laborious mental effort. The best way to have a conversation was one-to-one with no distractions so that the other person could give me his or her fullest attention and thus be patient as I paused and fished for words. A rare hour of "tea and talk" would totally wear me out, and yet those special times were the only times I really felt connected with the world outside my home. If friends noticed anything, maybe they thought I was tense or irritated or in a hurry to go – because I was, because trying to sound normal was so difficult. If a special tea and talk time was about familiar subjects, such as discussing spirituality and education with my friend Sue, it was easier to "get in the groove" and access that specific realm of vocabulary. Also, pausing to sit quietly and think fit that philosophical context.

When I did have conversations I often asked people, "Have I told you this already?" having no certainty of the content of our most recent conversations nor a clear memory of the order of personal contacts I had made.

One day in the summer of 2009, one month into taking 400 mg per day of the antibiotic Doxycycline Hyclate, I enjoyed three flowing, spontaneous, genuine, neighborly conversations with people in the grocery store! It was amazing! I was elated and grinning! It felt as if I were coming home from having been far, far away for a very long time. My doctor said I seemed like a different person.

14. Brain Fog

This painting portrays more properties of "brain fog." The images are all scenes from my past, so obviously I could

The Central Nervous System

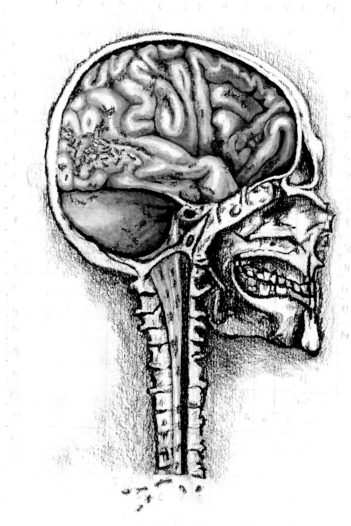

Borrelia burgdorferi

as

Myrmica rubra

15. The Central Nervous System, pencil and acrylic on art board, 16" x 20", 2010

remember them. Memories do not seem to become totally lost, but rather temporarily obscured, as if behind a veil. To put it another way, it is as if the "Files" still exist but the "Search/Find" command has been impaired. When asked to recall a simple fact on the spot, such as my son's birth date, it would frequently be impossible to remember as fast as I needed to. I "blanked out" on my own phone number while in the process of dialing home, and my child's date of birth when asked by the receptionist at the clinic. A difficulty I often faced while typing up my health notes and the early notes for my book was that I would "Select" a paragraph, "Cut" it, go to "Paste" it, but then forget where I was intending to put it and why. I'd have to put it back and retrace the whole thought process. Some periods were easier, but overall I was in a state of decline from 2001 to 2009. The "descent into becoming stupider" is what it felt like.

A friend offered this example of decreased cognitive functioning. He used to play chess against his computer at a genius level. During the month that he came down with Lyme he observed his deductive reasoning ability taking a mortal hit. His scores sank down to a beginner level, and he would find himself stumped, staring at the screen, barely able to focus. Although antibiotic treatment did relieve some of his physical symptoms, his scores have not yet risen, even though he has practiced by playing hundreds of games. He finds this very frustrating, but is now investigating herbal treatment and other alternative care that may help him recover more mental acuity.

Another quality of "brain fog" is the inability to focus on imagining an image, such as following a guided meditation or listening to directions about where to drive. Sometimes the inner mind-screen cannot hold an important image steady to build upon it, or it can appear like a blank, static TV screen that holds no images at all. Even when I was quiet and alone, sometimes random images would flutter by so fast it was as if a hyper toddler or monkey were running around with a video camera. Frequently my mind-screen was a crazy nebulous churning of strange images that made no sense. It was as if someone had poured some kind of super conductive fluid into my brain and suddenly neurons which had no relevant reason to connect were being activated. Whatever sensory stimulation

was introduced from the outside, such as looking around a room, hearing people talking, or being physically touched, the input did not dissolve and get renewed, but rather it continued to accumulate until it was overwhelming. It was as if my brain were a room full of fireworks floating in a sea of gas, and when one got lit they all went off.

Now, when I am well rested, my focus and memory work much better. I often find it easy to generate and edit my own creative writing. I'm learning to be more amused than concerned when files "go missing" (or the bag of frozen corn, which I recently found "filed" in the cabinet by the cat food instead of in the nearby freezer). I'm learning to be more aware of the "present moment" and trust that what I really need to know is what I do know right now. Sometimes the blank-mind state seems like a "free trial sample" of what some people may meditate for years to attain. Paradoxically, this messed-up-mind thing has not been all bad: it's gotten me to reflect upon who and what I really am.

15. The Central Nervous System

I admit that part of what inspired me to make this painting was my Lyme doctor saying, "Don't even try to get people to understand. Unless they've been through this, they just won't get it." Oh, what better challenge does the wounded-inner-child-as-artist need to incite her to try?

For this piece I started sketching from a photograph of Leonardo da Vinci's skull studies. The grid of numbers is a remnant of the process of doubling the size of the image. Leaving it in place seemed to add to the aura of a "scientific specimen," giving the ants even more of an invasive effect. (No matter how much we quantify and analyze our biological elements they continue to elude our attempts to fully control what happens to them.)

The font, Cochin, appears elegant and old fashioned as if written with a quill. In the process of transferring the writing using carbon paper, it got a bit of a wiggle that adds a "nervous" effect. It also reminds me of letters written by elderly

16. Party Pooper
acrylic and pencil on art board
16" x 20", 2010

relatives whose penmanship was elegant but is starting to reveal the atrophy of fine motor control – just like my hand writing under the influence of Lyme. If I held out my hands I could see as well as feel them trembling. In spite of these tremors, painting accurately was accomplished through bracing my hands and working slowly.

The idea of ants to represent Lyme bacteria had been with me for a long time – from journal entries trying to describe periods of cerebral irritation. "Ants in your pants" is a common metaphor. "Ants in the brain" is how it sometimes felt. *Myrmica rubra*, the stinging red ants which everyone in my community would recognize, seemed even more appropriate. Virtually every resident of Mount Desert Island has been through the visceral experience of being stung by a red ant, and knows how the stinging slowly resolves through an ebb and flow of lessening intensity but prolonged irritation.

Only a cutaway view of the brain would show the areas of mine seeming to be most affected, but I wanted a very alive-looking brain so I showed it from the outside. I didn't research areas and functions until after making this painting. It was amusing to discover that the highest density of ants was painted on the Primary Visual Cortex. Therefore a visual pun and a fun experience loop was unintentionally created: as we view this painting, the primary part of our brain processing this image is the Primary Visual Cortex – so, in a way, it becomes a self-portrait of whoever views it. (Whether they get it or not!)

16. Party Pooper

This painting began as a portrayal of "sensory overload." I wanted to depict the way I felt at a lovely luncheon which was the first big social event I had attempted in many months. As people gathered the noise level rose, and the din of voices and colors made me feel overwhelmed, dizzy, and slightly nauseated. I felt like an anxious animal wanting to find a place to hide, and chose to focus on the shelves of wonderful books in the hostess's house. As people came up to me initiating conversation I felt small and meek. I had a difficult time focusing on what they were saying, and an even harder time

thinking of something intelligent to reply. Stammering, shifty-eyed, I felt none of the mature poise I had possessed before the latest "Lyme Lowpoint." After that trial I decided (yet again) that I just wasn't up to socializing with groups any more, and so I avoided most gatherings until after starting medical treatment for Lyme in summer 2009. Attending a party, concert, play, puppet show, poetry reading, or community supper was a once-in-a-long-while venture, sapping energy banked up by extra rest and usually followed by a day or more of "falling apart," including fatigue, high anxiety, irritability, headaches, and tearfulness. Sometimes when I drove to buy groceries I would stall in the parking lot, realize that I was going to become too overwhelmed to function in the store, so I'd give up and drive home.

This painting, for me, represented positive future possibilities. It depicts warmth and good food, animated discussion and laughter. The very air is coming alive with dancing ribbons and dots of music. I saw it as a portrait of a buoyant celebration that I might enjoy again some day.

17. It's All in Your Head

This panel illustrates some of the situations and conditions I frequently experienced owing to the neurological symptoms of Lyme disease: On a small town main street, forgetting where the door was for a counseling appointment. Forgetting the counselor's name when asking a passerby for help (and I'd been there many times, including the week before). Spacing out while in the grocery store and looking in the refrigerator. "What was it I needed?" (Everybody spaces out sometimes, but this condition was daily.) Adding numbers mentally and not catching a ridiculous mistake. Becoming dizzy after climbing a short flight of stairs. Feeling tipsy all the time, as if slightly drunk, or as if I were in a little boat that was sloshing about in little waves. Losing my temper over sharp sounds such as a fork hitting the floor, reacting out of proportion to the event as if I were being physically attacked. Trembling visibly when trying to do fine motor tasks such as pouring vanilla extract while baking. Frequently feeling traumatized out of proportion to what was happening, and then feeling scared of being so

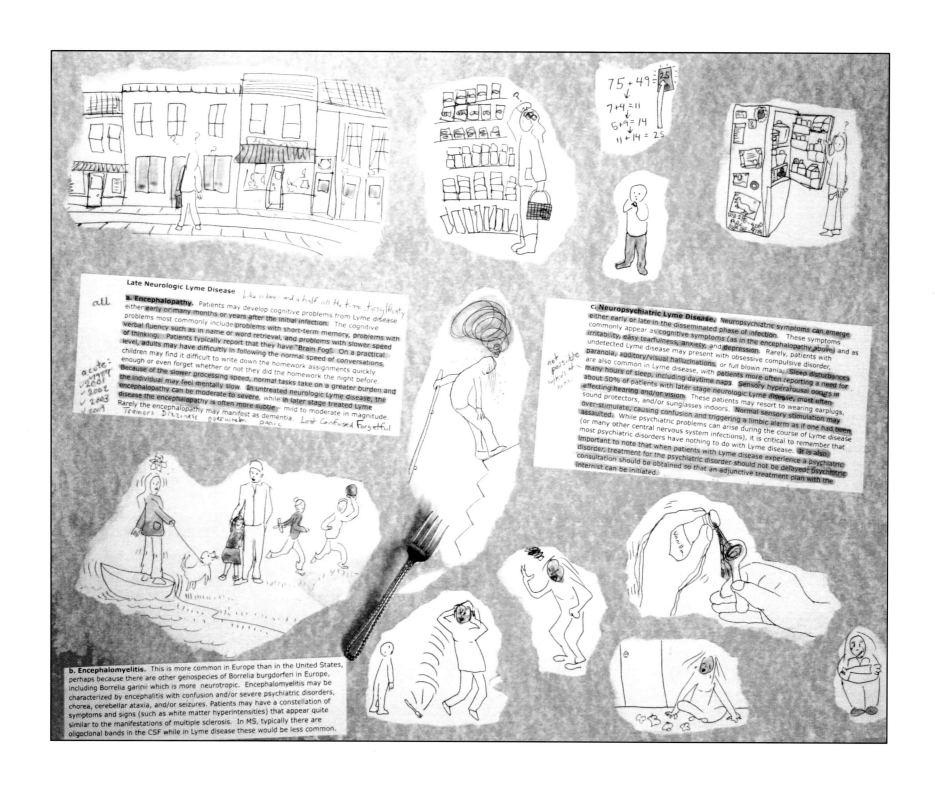

17. It's All in Your Head
acrylic, paper, pen, and highlighter pen on art board
16" x 20", 2010

highly sensitive and emotionally vulnerable.

Many people who are sick with Lyme have gone through the experience of being told by at least one doctor (if not many) that their "illness" is "all in their heads." Even people with obviously debilitating physical symptoms have been told that they are making it up: role playing, manifesting psychosomatic symptoms, creating attention-getting dramas.

My story plays a unique role in the emerging awareness of Lyme disease because for years I was the one trying to make it be "all in my head." I took all my symptoms personally. I believed that if I could only manage stress better and learn to maintain a more positive outlook on life – in other words, develop a more "mature and responsible attitude" – then my body would follow. I believed that if I tried hard enough to work on my "weaknesses" I would be able to turn things around and manifest health, wealth, long-term loving relationships, a nice house, and all that. So I just kept focusing on correcting the imbalances I perceived to be within myself and blaming myself for not being able to "get my act together." I did all this in private. There was no attention-seeking through complaining about my symptoms. To the contrary, for years I didn't let my closest friends, family members, or any doctor in on the story. I feared I would risk everything if I let down my guard. I might lose my job, friends' patience, clients' respect, possibly even custody of my baby. I believed I needed to show the world that I could "hold it all together" on my own.

Ironically, for most people with chronic Lyme, the disease is, quite literally, inside their heads: swarming colonies of tunnel-drilling spiral-shaped bacteria; and the neurotoxins they emit are wreaking havoc with their brains. This isn't something any of us can cure by simply "cultivating a positive attitude."

18. Asphyxiation

Before making the association between my symptoms and an illness, I often described sensations in metaphorical terms, interpreting them as psychosomatic side effects of "personal issues." I told one therapist that I often felt panic stricken when

there did not seem to be any outside trigger for it, and that sometimes for long periods of time I felt like a diver whose oxygen tank was empty or whose hose was blocked. Looking at that symbolically, I blamed stressful situations in my adult life and childhood, and examined where I was metaphorically "drowning" or "stifling" myself through self-limiting beliefs. But no matter how much I "let myself feel the feelings," journaled, emoted, or "aired out my issues" through talking, I got no lasting relief. I just didn't seem able to "process" fast enough to "get ahead" in the game and win improved health and ease. Periodically, as symptoms would flair up, I would appeal for help from the invisible realm; "Beam me up, I can't breathe down here!" I felt trapped in my body and desperate for relief.

While all that purging and processing may have helped on some levels, it was a *Eureka* moment to read that colonies of Lyme bacteria and other tick-borne parasites would sap oxygen from the host body, particularly the brain. My body was, quite literally, becoming "oxygen starved." Breathlessness, the feeling of not being able to get enough air, can be one of the physical symptoms of Lyme. (I do still often look at life metaphorically, and want to credit my angelic guardians for listening to my appeals for help and for leading me at the library to Pamela Weintraub's book about Lyme. The cosmic message that came with that nudge was, "You've learned what you can from this illness. Time to clean up the classroom.")

19. Poor Mother Deer

The two people most affected by all this were my children. Looking back, we do share many sweet memories: sewing a beautiful quilt, cooking and art projects, in-depth studies on topics of their passionate interests. Overall, I'm glad to have been at home with them for so much of their childhoods. But there were many days that even simple tasks could overwhelm me. During "Lyme lowpoints" I often felt breathless while reading aloud to my son. If he asked a question during the story, I might get irritated and weepy. Having to make the transition from focusing on the book, to focusing on his question, to finding my place in the book again, felt quite labor intensive! I often explained to my children that I was "stressed

18. Asphyxiation, acrylic on art board, 20" x 16", 2009

19. Poor Mother Deer
paper and acrylic on birch
16" x 20", 2010

out" and needed to take a "time out" alone, if possible. For several years I believed we were home-schooling because it was what *they* needed, but looking back I admit it was also because I didn't feel capable, competent, or confident doing any work outside the house, and home-schooling made me feel "respectfully employed." Compared to most other home-schooling families we were very house-bound. We almost never traveled or attended events with other people. For a while when my son was a toddler, I tried attending a parent/child play group, but I could barely think straight when there. In the recreation room at a local church where we met the lights, sounds, and activity level made my head swirl. I felt dizzy, mute, anxious, and shy, and couldn't remember most people's names from one week to the next. Eventually we stopped going. "Barely coping" was passing for "normal"!

In spring 2009, before I learned about Lyme, I decided to enroll my children in public school for the fall, knowing I just didn't have the strength or mental ability to be a good home-school teacher any longer. People started asking, "What are you going to do with all that free time – go back to work or school?" And I would think, "Sleep – or die." There was no motivation to do anything else. It felt as if my only motivation for staying in a body was to see my children grow up.

Once the treatment for Lyme was underway and my mind began clearing, I began to see the impact of my illness on my children. I began to solicit more professional support such as informing their teachers about the effects of Lyme. One of my daughter's teachers asked her if she was aware of how often she finished other people's sentences. Fortunately she had the perspective to laugh with me as we realized the conditioning she'd gotten from being around my "special needs" all day. At the recommendation of a friend I initiated contact with a social and health services agency which sent a case worker to make house calls. With her sympathetic and compassionate support I began to open up to even more help such as family counseling. It required huge courage for me to let people in to witness my private world and I felt very vulnerable when admitting I needed help. But the more I did, the more grateful I

became to receive that support. Family counseling supported us in finding new *healthy* norms.

The idea for this painting arrived one day as I went for a walk in a cemetery near my home and saw deer tracks in the snow. I started thinking of all the deer with Lyme and that they might feel as badly as I did. Suddenly the cartoon image of a deer family came to mind and I bolted happily home to begin this painting. Every time I look at it I can't stop laughing. Since I made this painting it has been pointed out to me that although domesticated mammals such as dogs, cats, and horses do show symptoms of Lyme disease, infected deer and other wild carriers of *Bb* such as raccoons and mice do not seem to show symptoms of suffering from the illness.

20. Fight/Flight

I wanted to depict the incoherent storminess of feeling trapped by illness and yet struggling to find peace of mind and courage. I envisioned a painting with hurricane-like swirls of black and white with little colorful objects sticking out. I found the heart-shaped shield in a parking lot that morning as I walked my son to school. Then I discovered a little box of collage bits (gathered years before, for a different project) which all worked perfectly in this one! Expressing my inner struggle visually was incredibly uplifting. My willingness to trust inspiration increased because of the way this painting came together – it was healing to have such a coherent creative experience! This illustrates how healing can be experienced on the level of the mind, in spite of physical symptoms, and how being willing to look at what is most difficult can begin to transform it.

I wish that everyone recovering from any serious or chronic illness could talk about it with a counselor because trauma can accumulate just from being ill, and this trauma can also be released in many ways. I knew I needed help with this; I couldn't just take medicine to get better. Also, anxiety is one of the dominant symptoms of Lyme disease. One feels anxious even *before* there is a cause – it's as if a thumb is already pushing the fight/flight button. Neurotoxins from the bacteria in the brain may be one cause.

20.Fight/Flight
acrylic, paper metal, cloth, plastic, and feather on art board on birch
16" x 20", 2010

21. Insomnia
acrylic, cloth, and paper on art board
16" x 20", 2010

After I had been on medicine for long enough to regain the ability to speak articulately again, one-to-one counseling became another useful experience that supported me in reassessing my outlook on life. I could share what I'd been through and reevaluate my life with a rational and compassionate witness. This bolstered my confidence considerably. Even though I continued to have neurological "rough patches," I learned to acknowledge that it was based on a hypersensitive body; the problem was not a personal issue to be self-critical about. When the anxiety got aimed at specific problems that then snowballed into angst, I learned to disengage from any serious decision making and wait until the storm had passed. Sleep aids and anxiety medication also helped my body remember what "calm" is, so now I can "find this place on the dial" more easily on my own.

21. Insomnia

Insomnia was the inspiration for the first painting I made in January 2010. Although my health had significantly improved, I still wasn't exactly feeling great. Daily household tasks and parenting were taking most of my energy, and I was trying to fit in a daily nap if possible. I hadn't painted much since the initial burst of inspiration in the summer of 2009. But the paints and brushes looked so enticing that I finally gave in and sat down.

How can I paint when I'm still so sore and tired, I wondered. Suddenly, the vision came of a darkened room with tiny colored squares floating above a bed, representing the endless streams of thought that seem to flow when one is too tired to focus but too wired to drift off to sleep. Okay, I thought, that's a nice image. I can relate to that. But what about the colored squares? Magazine clippings? I didn't have any in the house, having jettisoned most of my collage supplies the previous summer. Then the mail came, and in the box was a catalog, full of little colorful squares with the most perfect images! Using a razor blade I cut out almost every one and by bedtime had finished the collage. Rather than overcoming symptoms in order to do art, art emerged as a way to honor the struggle. That got the momentum going. Within two months, all the other paintings for the exhibit had been completed!

22. Sleep – Assembly Instructions

During the initial health history interview I was asked if I used extra pillows at night. "Yes," I replied, thinking that was all. "How many? Where?" my new doctor prompted, looking very serious. I had to stop and think. It was both amusing and gratifying to let someone in on those ridiculous facts of bedding down! It had become a nightly ceremony. It started with a body pillow when I was pregnant and over time I added four more pillows. Sleeping was not simple, it was an installation project! The goal was proper placement and elevation of parts to reduce the strain on tender nerves and sore joints.

Having pillow combo and placement down to a science, my doctor and I began addressing the insomnia and pain management part of the scheme. In *The Power of Now* (2004) Eckhart Tolle recommends being present with pain instead of just trying to make it go away, and he explains that this awareness will help dissolve the "pain body." Sometimes I do that, at other times I take strong analgesics. I've come to accept a phrase I used to pooh-pooh, "better living through chemistry." Valerian tincture, lemon balm and lavender tea, Clonazepam, Advil, Extra Strength Tylenol – whatever it takes, I'm willing to give it a try! Sometimes one thing works for a while, then after a while it doesn't. In any case, getting more sleep at night and resting more during the day have been essential to the healing process. Over a year into treatment I still used all those pillows but the left side of my body was usually free of pain. Oddly, the right side, from head to toe, still ranged from slightly strained and numb to highly painful and "scraped," depending on how much activity I had engaged in, whether I was fighting "what's going around," and how much rest I'd gotten recently. Napping still feels out-of-character and rather lazy, but maybe that will change with more practice!

This painting was fun to make. The style was inspired by IKEA furniture assembly instructions. Creating it was a therapeutic challenge. Sometimes my left hand was trembly, another neurological symptom. It could be steadied by holding the other end of the paintbrush with my right hand (I'm left-handed), or by bracing my hand on the paper. These tremors

47

22. Sleep – Assembly Instructions
acrylic and permanent marker on birch
16" x 20", 2010

23. Helping Hands
acrylic on birch
16" x 20", 2010

were not detectable when I used firm pressure, such as drawing with pen or making broad or rapid strokes of paint. They were most disruptive when I was trying to paint the white background accurately into tiny corners. I listened to soothing piano music and worked in short segments with stretch breaks, meditatively painting over the whole image three times.

Over the course of the first year of treatment these tremors improved a lot. They would only flair up during episodes of high stress, heightened nerve sensitivity, not getting enough rest, or in the midst of an additional immune challenge such as catching a cold – which implies still having some periods of tremors within an average week, just not a constant condition.

23. Helping Hands

Therapeutic Massage, Reiki, Shiatsu, and Craniosacral Therapy were very effective in helping me find inner calm and integrate so much change as I began to heal. For three years, before learning about Lyme I had considered going to an Osteopath who was helping some of my friends who suffered from nerve pain and migraines. Finally, as I was working on these paintings in early 2010, I got around to making an appointment. The D.O.'s subtle, noninvasive touch improved the flow of cerebral-spinal fluid around my brain which helped "dissolve" the feeling of "mental discombobulation." It was so affirming to hear from a trained professional that my private experience of inner mental and emotional turbulence had some detectable physiological evidence! It was also interesting to be told that earlier treatments wouldn't have helped. There had been so much physical imbalance that I needed to have been on medications such as antibiotics first, for a while, before the nervous system was stable enough to make use of this kind of subtle energetic support. I said perhaps that is why I hadn't come in before. "Yes, your body knew," the D.O. said. An image that came to me during that first session was that the damaged nervous system is like a cat that gets scared up a tree by a fierce barking dog (infections and trauma). Antibiotics are a dog catcher, and the Osteopath is a firefighter who gently persuades the kitty that it's safe to come down now. This painting is based on imagery that came to mind during my second session, involving many emotionally charged images and the acceptance of support for releasing them.

24. Side Effects

A common antibiotic for treating Lyme, Doxycycline Hyclate, makes one highly sensitive to sunlight. During the first week on it, I called the clinic to ask if it was normal to feel a sort of icy wind or mild burning sensation on my hands and was told yes, that was a possible side effect. Having a little boy and a part-time summer gardening job, I couldn't exactly stay inside all day as advised, so I tried wearing sunblock. Until I read *The Lyme Disease Solution* by Kenneth B. Singleton M.D., M.P.H. (2008), chock full of self-help details, I didn't understand that sunblock wouldn't help. But by then my hands and face were badly burned. It took six months to recover, including growing new thumbnails. I invested in some soft, silky, sun-proof clothing including broad-brimmed hats and light-weight gloves to wear every time I went out on a sunny day.

A second side effect of all the health challenges I've been through and all the methods of healing I've tried is that a lifetime worth of stifled anger has been burning away. Underneath the frozen layers of denial, grief, and depression lay a red hot lava layer of anger. With every step of physical healing I have found that there is an emotional counterpart of release, then a phase of reintegration.

A third side effect of being ill and dealing with a long period of treatment is that it induced me to seek solace and comfort beyond the (seemingly unattainable) physical level. I have felt it to be very important to address personal, psychological, and spiritual needs to further establish an environment of healing inside and around me. I loved *The Disappearance of the Universe*, by Gary Renard, and *The Interior Castle*, by St. Teresa of Avila, translated by Mirabi Starr. Although St. Teresa lived five hundred years before me, her descriptions of her own health challenges and the spiritual experiences she was going through gave me much counsel and encouragement. Learning about the "Inquiry" process as described by teacher Byron Katie has also played a key role in how I deal with anger and

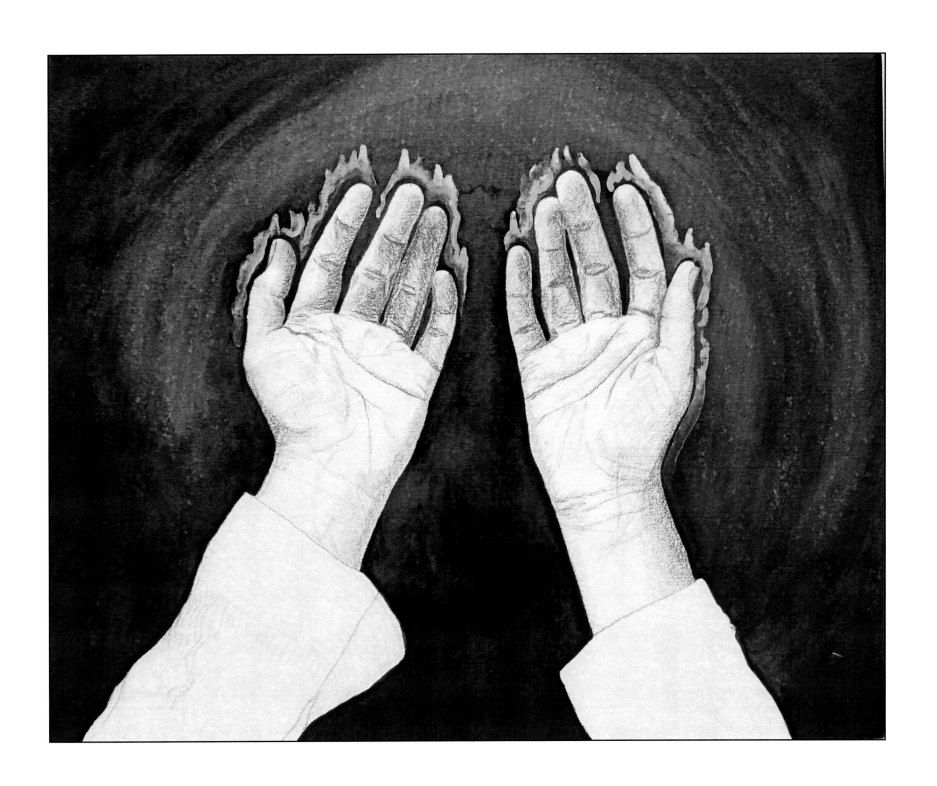

24. Side Effects
acrylic and pencil on art board
16" x 20", 2010

fear, particularly regarding the future of my health. It has been comforting to have examples of how to look at life differently, which supports me in accepting what I am going through at the same time as I'm finding the courage to make changes in my life and ask for help.

A fourth side effect of entering the healing process is that my life has been "lit" from within; I'm learning to trust intuition and inspiration more than ever before. I've been "on fire" with enthusiasm to be creative and to communicate. This painting was fun to have lying on my desk in the art studio; the open hands kept receiving all manner of objects!

25. Path of Recovery

When I get very run down, all the color goes out of life; everything seems dull, devoid of vitality and meaning. I feel no emotional connection with anything or anyone, even my children. Before I began treatment for Lyme, this state had become the norm. I could act happy to be polite, but those feelings weren't really there. Looking back I now interpret it as the immune system being overwhelmed and trying to send me the signal to stop trying to distract myself, to get down to business and attend to the "state of emergency." There simply was no extra fuel for anything but surviving.

The summer I began treatment, I also began to experience random breakthroughs into vitality and well-being, which literally seemed to bring more color into life. I don't mean that my vision had been literally reduced to black and white, the change was perhaps more about having the capacity for linking visual data with emotional connectedness. The switch was from having no feeling, just numbness, flatness, to being able to appreciate beauty and take pleasure in seeing nature's colors again. From a couple of random hours per week in the beginning, to several hours at a time several days per week, my life increased in color and vitality.

As my mind cleared more and more, I engaged more with the world around me. There was still physical pain, but month by month there were significant improvements. I kept a daily chart

of symptoms, so it might be that on a scale of 1-10 the pain was a "5" instead of an "8." In the beginning, any amount of exercise, such as walking around the block, could leave me hobbling. After a while the inflammation was reduced so that more days than not I could take a longer walk, enjoy it, and feel refreshed instead of drained. My hands and arms no longer ached constantly.

Even after months of treatment, common symptoms were mild to severe arthritis, mild nausea, temperature swings, sore muscles, achy joints and achy bones, pressure in the spine and head, and random nerve pain. But compared with before treatment, it was the difference between being so sick as to not even want a body, to rediscovering an interest in life and having a sense of curiosity about the future, even if feeling ill.

About five seasons into treatment I experienced nearly nearly three pain-free weeks for the first time in years! I was able to swim and hike without paying for it later. That wonderful taste of having a body which was simply a vehicle for relishing life did not endure, but it was a window into the possibility of what could lie ahead.

A year and a half into treatment I described my body as having a "fragile state of health" that was easily upended by stress or exposure to common illnesses. If I overdid it, such as a three-hour drive around town doing chores, that day and the next I would become easily flustered and irritable, hypersensitive to touch, light, and sound, my skull and the base and top of my spine became sore, and my whole right side would start to feel irritated and strained. If the stress continued and I could not stop to lie down and rest soon, that strained feeling became a raw, burning sensation from head to toe. Colds could still last for weeks. So I continued to live a very low-key life style compared with most people my age, staying at home reading, writing, and resting while my children were in school.

The change I was most grateful for was that my emotional and mental stability was more reliable; as long as I was well rested I was able to think clearly and communicate in the moment in a way that felt intelligent and "tuned in." Cranial irritation and

25. Path of Recovery
acrylic on art board
16" x 20", 2010

headaches were sometimes persistent, but they became less severe. Friends of mine with Lyme attested to the possibility that I might feel even stronger and more resilient in the days to come, but they also illustrated the possibility that going off antibiotic treatment for more than a few months might mean plunging back into the depths.

26. 63 Days

This painting was an experiment to chart illness and health visually by choosing one dominant image to sum up each day, (November 1, 2009 to January 2, 2010). I wanted to describe "the nature of the beast" to my family so they could be aware of the "two steps forward, one step back" journey of healing. The bacteria can exist in several forms or stages, such as cysts, and can hide deep inside tissues. Switching to a new medication to smoke them out of hiding or attack them at a different part of their life cycle can cause a sudden die-off and then these toxic substances have to be flushed out of the system. For several days one may plunge back into intense symptoms. This is called a "Herxheimer" effect. Knowing about it in advance and letting others know when it is occurring can be helpful psychologically – to know that this is really a good thing, a "sign of success." (It is also at this point that a person with only a clinical diagnosis of chronic Lyme may at last get a "positive" blood test.) The goal of informing others became secondary to what I received. In creating this calendar I gained the perspective that, even if there were difficult days there would also be easier times ahead, and in spite of pain "life would go on" through the seasons and holidays. This visual reminder helped me have more patience and perspective.

27. Healing Supports

There is no universal protocol for effectively treating Lyme disease. I've heard of people treating it homeopathically, with herbal medicines, ozone steam saunas, hyperbaric oxygen therapy, Rife/Bare machines, and other methods. Everyone I've talked to who is treating it with allopathic medicines is taking different antibiotics on a different schedule, even if they have the same doctor. We're all taking a different array of supplements and making a variety of differing dietary choices. Some people try many things and don't get well. Others take one prescription for a short time and seem to be cured. It is interesting to hear about other people's successes through different choices, and what they believe in and why. A positive side effect of the epidemic is that more people than ever are having to consider more aspects of the healing process and more of a range of choices to support that healing. It is making people become more self-aware instead of just following a standard prescription and taking "doctor's orders."

I believe everyone who gets Lyme will have his or her own unique treatment and process of healing, and that this is not likely to change. Lyme, like syphilis, can have many different effects in different parts of the body. There is the compounding issue of co-infections, which may or may not respond to the same treatment as the *Bb* bacteria. Different people's immune systems are in different states of health at the time of initial infection. Furthermore, there is the issue of how long a person may have been ill or misdiagnosed, perhaps allowing time for the invaders to become more deeply entrenched or resistant to certain treatments.

Just "killing germs" isn't enough to make a person well. I believe taking probiotics every night before bed is a must for anyone taking antibiotics for any length of time. Although some people get diarrhea from antibiotics, I never suffered from that side effect and my digestion was much better than it had been for years. I took the second dose of antibiotics with a small meal about 5:00 p.m., then, just before bed, on an empty stomach, I took probiotics with a light snack, usually also with probiotic rich *kefir*. I would also recommend live sauerkraut, especially for people who cannot do dairy.

Professionals such as Dr. Pat Gerbarg and Dr. Richard P. Brown are investigating and sharing the importance of repairing the body's damaged tissues and strengthening the immune system with complementary herbal medicines, nutritional supplements, and yoga. As I've contemplated what my body and immune system have been through, I've imagined a different label than "Lyme disease" to describe the

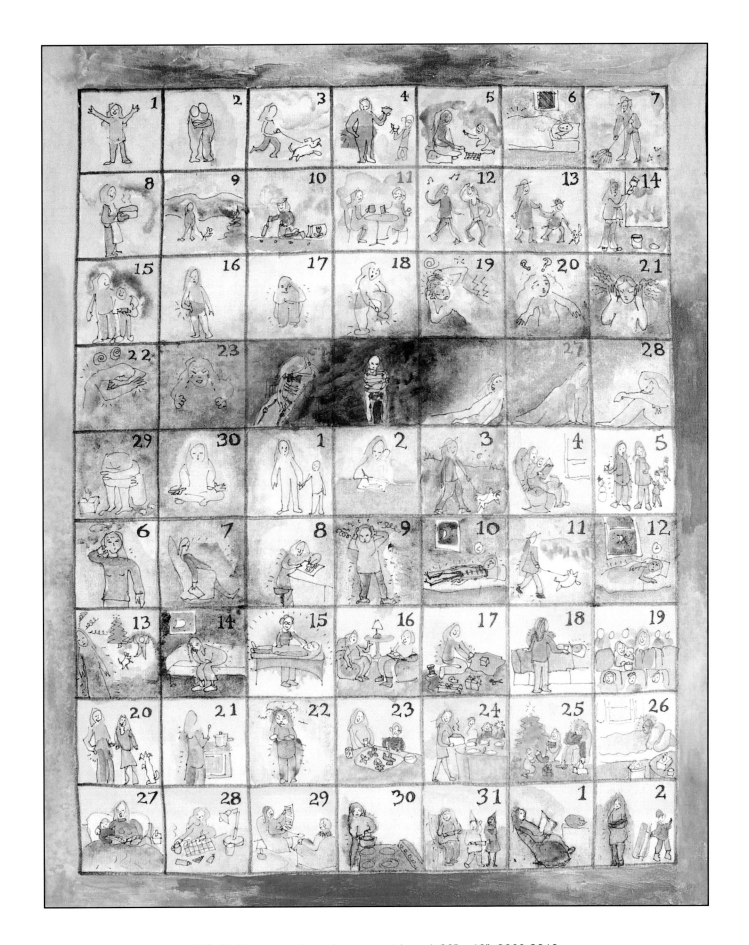

26. 63 Days, acrylic and pen on art board, 20" x 16", 2009-2010

situation: "Immune S.O.S." standing for "Immune System Overload Syndrome," in which multiple pathogens are involved and the human body is viewed as an out-of-balance microcosm in need of support on many levels, possibly for an extended period of time, possibly with antibiotics, antivirals, and other natural medications and alternative holistic therapies.

During one of my checkups an intern joined the meeting. As I answered questions, my doctor put them in context for him. "That's a typical complaint for Lyme – we hear this frequently." I turned to the intern and asked, "So, are you going to become a Lyme Aware doctor, too?" "Nooooo!" He said, raising his hands in a startled reflex, as if "going there" amounted to touching hot coals. Most doctors are wary of litigation should they treat their patients with antibiotics beyond the official Centers for Disease Control's limited protocol. Lyme disease is still a highly controversial subject. The award winning documentary about Lyme, *Under Our Skin* examines some of this, as does Weintraub's book *Cure Unknown: Inside the Lyme Epidemic.*

Even though my doctor claimed to not be "Lyme literate, but rather "Lyme aware", with much more to learn, I trusted that I was being offered the best information and recommendations available at the time. (Some were acceptable to my insurance company, others were not covered so I did not try them.) We were collaborative partners in the choice making. I accepted that many choices were being left up to me, such as which supplements (and which brands) to take. I understood that we were both pioneers. All along I have researched possibilities, discussed choices, and tried things that were easily available. One of the biggest changes I've gone through in the learning process with Lyme is that I no longer draw a hard line between the physical and the ephemeral, the world of allopathic medicine and various holistic sects. Now I'm much more open to using whatever seems to help and what I feel drawn to trying. I use intuition to guide my choice making, and that is an important element of "taking responsibility" for myself. Along with a multitude of supplements and prescription medications, I have deeply appreciated whatever hands-on support I've been able to afford, such as Therapeutic Massage, Shiatsu, Craniosacral Therapy, Osteopathy, and Acupuncture.

Other things that have been helpful are daily hot baths, with Epsom Salts and Hydrogen peroxide once or twice a week; hot packs for sore muscles and along the spine; lying down more; short walks; daily sunlight; talking with friends; being cozy with my children; personal reflection and writing time; spiritual study and meditation; counseling to help reprogram my outlook on life and get me out of the post-traumatic-stress-disorder rut; Bach Rescue Remedy; avoiding toxins (especially petrochemicals) by traveling and driving as little as possible and staying out of smelly stores; eating more raw greens, nuts, and seeds, and eating less sugar, dairy, and wheat; eating organic food as much as affordable; and getting subscriptions to Netflix and The Funny Times for comic relief! I have found it to be very important to address personal, psychological, and spiritual needs to further establish an environment of healing inside and around me.

28. Mindsets

In this exhibit, this is the only piece of art from another era of my life. For me it appears to be a sort of preview or map of many things that have happened since then. I made this collage before I had children and pets, but pictured are images which could represent the core members of my household: a girl, a boy, a dog, and a cat, linked to me by golden threads. I will not interpret any more, for this was a purely fanciful art-therapy play time that I had alone one day. I see new meaning every time I look at it. That's kind of what the piece is about – looking at things differently, and that the way we look at things can reveal new meaning. The reason this collage made its way into the Lyme-Light exhibit is the idea of mindsets. Having a disease with a neurological component has brought me to the depths of considering mindsets. It has induced me to investigate my thinking and my beliefs about who I am, what I have control over, and what surrender means.

To add further paradox to the discussion of "It's All In Your Head," I believe, after all this expression of gratitude for

27. Healing Supports
acrylic, photos, paper, wood, lace, glass, leaf, shell, plastic, and bark on canvas and wood
16" x 20", 2010

modern medicine, that healing always begins at the level of the mind. I believe my process of healing began before medication, with the choice to risk reconnecting with life again – my own and others' – and with surrendering to the urgent volition to seek new information and persist in asking for help. This trek through new behavioral territory still takes courage sometimes, but the healing process seems to have a momentum of its own. The more I share, the better life feels. Instead of trying to hide what I am going through and judging it as "good" or "bad," I'm learning to simply be honest with myself and other people. Coming out of denial is like finally breathing after holding my breath for a long time – breathing into all those old stuck places – breathing into the darkness and breathing back into life.

There are many things we cannot directly control when we are ill, but there are some questions we may ask and some choices we may make about how to look at our lives: What role is this illness playing in my life? What might I learn from it? Who might I be without it? Do I really want to heal? If I begin healing, am I really willing for my life to change in ways I can't predict? Am I open to trying something new, to receiving support from a different source?

Healing may involve different things for different people. It may include stopping playing doctor to oneself at home, finally letting a professional help. It may involve becoming willing to try a new form of treatment outside one's familiar realm of faith and experience. It may entail surrendering into acceptance of illness and pain. It may even include facing the inevitability of death. As one's physical body declines, one may go through a process of coming to peace with one's life and becoming able to experience serenity and spiritual well-being in spite of illness. Healing physically may involve a process of personal empowerment, enduring an initiation process, going on a "hero's journey" that transforms not only one's own life but the very terrain for those who follow.

At this time I have no regrets about the way illness has swerved me away from some experiences and toward others. Although illness prevented me from taking certain paths of action, the limitations it imposed skewed me toward the openings I did take, and in those I often flourished. While teaching, for example, my own cognitive struggles have made me sympathetic and sensitive to the unique learning styles of each of my students. Being orally compromised (forgetting words, speaking haltingly) – not all the time, but enough to undermine my confidence to enter certain professional and social arenas – enhanced my focus on visual and written communication.

Rather than pressing outward into the world – climbing a career ladder, seeking further formal education, getting into a busy and complicated social life – the conditions of my health have skewed me toward more private, self-paced creativity and self-directed study. Through acknowledging (gradually, with setbacks as reminders) my body's need for a low key life-style (very little travel or group activities or socializing), I've had more time for quiet reflection and contemplation than most people can carve out in their middle years. My depth of focus on the inner or spiritual life may not have become so intense had I been more able to participate comfortably and successfully in activities out in the world. Nevertheless, besides the effects of chronic illness, I can also look back with gratitude for the amazing journeys I've taken – around the world and within relationships – so, overall I feel I've lived a very rich life.

29. Letting Go

This last painting in the series is about much more than Lyme. In fact, it is symbolic of life beyond Lyme. Letting go of labeling myself as a "Lyme patient" or an "ill person." Letting go of focusing so much on symptoms. Letting go of focusing on the past. Letting go of my stories as defining permanent meaning. Letting go of worrying about what effects this story may have in the world and how that may influence me. Letting go of the need to judge each step of what happens as a "failure" or a "success." Letting go of the burden of attachment to a particular future outcome in return for the freedom of not knowing. Even letting go of defining this as "a time of healing."

28. Mindsets, watercolor, pencil, crayon, thread, yarn, staples, and paper on watercolor paper, 22" x 22", 1994

This image also illustrates a wonderful paradox that one may experience on many levels: that sometimes when something is let go of, it ceases to have substance any longer. Even something as consuming as pain, as heavy as guilt, as dwarfing as shame, as monstrous as fear, as solid as ignorance, can dissolve into thin air and become nothing. If transformation is truly desired, much is possible beyond the limits of our rational understanding. In spite of and even through illness, there can be opening of hearts and minds.

~ end of original story ~

29. Letting Go
acrylic and paper on art board
16" x 20", 2010

Further Reflections on Healing

Looking Back from the Present

Today as I sit in the sunny upstairs office, sipping a warm mug of medicinal Heavenly Bamboo and Sacred Basil tea, the birds are singing so loudly that their songs penetrate the heavy storm windows. You can tell that spring is on the way, even though there is still some snow on the ground. I'm thoroughly enjoying writing updates for this book and choosing which new artwork to include. As I assemble these pages, it's a time to reflect on how far I've come in just five years.

At this time of year, five years ago, I was too ill to care about living – except for hoping to see my children grow up. I hadn't a clue what was wrong, or how to fix it. All of my willpower was spent just getting through another minute, hour, and day. Where might I be now without having taken antibiotics for more than a month or two? What if I had been told that I just needed to accept my symptoms for the rest of my life as "post-Lyme syndrome"? As it is, every year has been better than the previous one. I hope that my updated story offers other people who are ill new hope, and possibly some new perspectives or ideas that lead to their further healing.

For now my children and I are thriving. My son is happily homeschooling, which includes memorizing multiplication tables, and meeting with an intuitive healer who mentors him in working with the healing properties of crystals! My daughter is attending a United World College, in a castle in Wales, with free tuition and board. She's a gifted social organizer, and motivated to work on some of the world's most challenging problems. For me, now, every week includes some creative endeavors, and a sustainable rhythm of tutoring, teaching art, giving and teaching Reiki, and playing clarinet in a community orchestra. Every day includes loving interactions with family and friends. There seems to be so much to live for now – and the vitality to enjoy participating!

Four years ago, at this time of year, the original exhibit of "In the Lyme-Light: Portraits of Illness and Healing" was on display for the first time at College of the Atlantic. As people mingled at the reception, drinking lime-aid, I sat near the guest book, chatting with my friend Kirsten. Her radiant smile and golden boing-boing curls defied the fact that she was also being treated for Lyme – and soon would be battling cancer. She had reached out to encourage me when I was most doubtful that I could go on, and had offered to help me with a fundraiser. We organized a screening of *Under Our Skin* for the first day of spring, and in anticipation of that I was motivated to finish the art exhibit in time to display it concurrently.

Now a photo of Kirsten sits by my computer as encouragement to finish this book. The image is printed on the front of a program from her recent memorial service. Knowing that her body was dying, she helped plan the service, choosing the caterer, musicians, and dancers, the food, songs, and poems. As other community members noted, her presence could be felt among us. She was nowhere in particular, yet seemed everywhere at once. Attending this "Service of Celebration" prompted me to get on with living and loving to the fullest, and doing whatever I can to be of service. While there are other subjects besides Lyme that I would love to write and paint about, revising this book and "getting it out there" is "where the energy is at." It is pleasurable to acknowledge and work in harmony with that. Things tend to fall into place when I do.

It's been three years since my original book was published. Later that summer, in 2011, my doctor asked if I had painted lately. No, not in about a year and a half. So she gave me a prescription, in a sincere voice, "Get out some paints, sit down in front of a canvas, and see what happens." A new series emerged. Most of it is included in the following pages. These paintings are about healing and transformation in a broader sense, not specifically about Lyme, although painting them was part of the healing process. Making art was a way to explore, express, and honor the transformations I was going through. These transformations were partly physical, but they also included a metamorphosing sense of self, sometimes the absence of self altogether, a heightened awareness and integration of higher sensory perceptual abilities, an altered approach to decision making, and discovering how to access unconditional peace and well-being.

It's been two full years since I went off all antibiotics. After making much progress during the nearly three years on various antibiotics aimed at Lyme and other tick borne diseases, I'd reached a plateau. I had also gone through many internal psychological changes, and felt stable and confident enough to "take off the wet bandage," to see how my body would do without the supporting influence allopathic medicine. My doctor agreed that it was worth trying. During the spring of 2012 I also did a thorough allergy elimination dietary evaluation to identify food allergies and sensitivities. This gave me one more way to have some control over inflammation.

Another dietary change was adding sauerkraut – filled with probiotics – to my daily diet. I used to think I hated sauerkraut. But that was the dead, limp, colorless, canned kind. When I first opened a jar of the live, bright, fresh, homemade version, I stood in the kitchen forking it up, straight from the jar, as I might have spooned up ice-cream! I craved it so much that I learned how to make it. Since then I've also learned to make natural ginger ale and a version of "fire cider," a marinade of raw apple cider vinegar with grated garlic, ginger, onion, and daikon root. I feel that these homemade tonics contribute to the continued gut and upper respiratory health I enjoy. I rarely have any digestive ailments, colds, flues, sore throats, or sinus infections, even though I'm going out into the world more often.

Speaking of going out into the world, it's been one year, exactly, since I completed a college level course, "Teaching Students with Disabilities," and passed it with an A. Even though the pace of my reading, writing, and studying for this course took all my available effort, my head was clear enough to think straight, and my hands did not shake when I took notes! Although I got spacey by the end of each evening class, I had the vocabulary to advocate for my needs, and my teacher kindly made accommodations. The course was part of my self-directed "professional rehab" program, and it led to feeling more prepared and confident as a private academic tutor. It

also turned out to be therapeutic, a forum to reflect upon and name more of the conditions I had experienced – and it made me wonder how many students with learning disabilities are actually struggling with neurological Lyme symptoms.

I've become an advocate for Lyme awareness locally, encouraging schools, day cares, and camps to teach students to do tick checks when they venture into their back yards, public play areas, and our gorgeous Acadia National Park. My goal is to promote practical self-care and awareness, not fear. Likewise, by sharing my stories of illness and healing, my goal is not to incite fear, but rather to offer encouragement. I can't take away anyone's pain or offer a recipe for anyone else's healing, but I can share what I've tried that's worked and reveal more of the insights and breakthroughs that my healing process revealed. Not all of my shifts were *because* of Lyme, but a good many happened within the context of *healing from it*. And, some of the psychological and energetic shifts have helped to strengthen my physical immune system, helping it overcome Lyme from the inside. Some of the most difficult passages I went through turned out to have beneficial results.

Now there is an inner flame of vitality in my belly, and a palpable presence of loving warmth infusing and enfolding my body. No matter what is happening, there is access to an enduring sense of even-keel well-being. I still live, as we all do, moment by moment, hour by hour, day by day, but there is no longer an urgency to escape, no more longing for release. Most of the time, instead of struggling with illness, there is calm alertness, flowing creativity, and heartfelt presence. Instead of feeling victimized by illness, caught in a web of trauma, and overwhelmed by life's challenges, I feel open to the unfolding mystery of life, day by day, available to be worked through and loved through moment by moment, and an almost constant underlying sense of gratitude. Sometimes doing nothing and just *being* is almost too sweet to bear, so I go back to focusing on current sensory impressions and engaging in whatever tasks are at hand. This evening that includes typing on the computer at this wooden desk, letting the dog out into the dark back yard, feeling gentle misty rain on my face, hearing the chorus of frogs, and smelling spring in the air.

Standing in Both Worlds

The painting "Standing in Both Worlds" explores several dualities. Left/right, internal/external, color/darkness, structure/formlessness. We see the skeletal structure of the body and the outer form of the head. One half of the skeleton is painted over bright swirls of color, the other half is painted over a dark amorphous background. The background represents an inner or outer environment that affects the person in different ways. Even though bones would be inside a body, "in the dark," they are painted in clear sparkly glitter glue. Becoming conscious of scanning our interior bodily environment "lights it up" with our awareness. Becoming aware of the interior landscape can promote healing. The person faces into the darkness, with eyes open, willing to see, rather than to avoid it.

When I published my first book, I was two years into treatment. Relative to rock bottom, I had made much progress. But some areas of healing which I thought I had already "accomplished" did not endure. Most perplexing was the persistent right-sided pain that would flair up severely at times, triggering dizziness and spaciness, as well as simply making it hard for me to concentrate because of the pain itself. Since the left side of my body had become normal, virtually pain-free, I couldn't attribute the right-sided problem – nor the left-sided resolution – to anything in particular that I had or had not done right! Furthermore, reading about how *Bb* was so stealthy at hiding deep inside tissues and cells in the body, it didn't seem likely that I would *ever* be completely free of it. My immune system still wasn't operating robustly, even with antibiotic and antiviral support. So, optimism battled with hopelessness about becoming healthier.

One day, extremely tired of the drama of feeling terrible on one side, I asked my body what was up with the right-sided pain? Was I just a helpless victim of circumstance, destined to struggle with meaningless pain? Or was there some important message to become aware of encoded in that pain? I had asked before, but not quite as earnestly, not quite as open to hearing *anything*. Obviously I *consciously* wanted to heal, but I set the intention to become aware of any other *unconscious*

intentions. Suddenly the idea surfaced that I was "standing in both worlds." Half of me had the will to live, but mostly for the sake of my children – not, to be honest, for my own sake. The death wish was equally strong. There was a thought that it would be easier to die than to face the daunting tasks of inhabiting a vulnerable body, rebuilding a career and a new social life – starting over almost a decade after I'd pulled out.

The book I was reading, Bernie Seigal's *Love, Medicine and Miracles*, presented a personal challenge. I related to the profiles of his patients who *didn't* do very well; the ones who had not yet affirmed a strong desire to live and recover. Thus began a new level of conscious participation in healing, different from taking medicines, resting, and passively receiving alternative treatments from other healers. I needed to turn toward accepting and embracing my life, and life in this body, such as it was, prior to having proof that my body would feel better and thus be "worth" inhabiting. This led to much inner work, since directing attention into my body, mind, heart, and gut area each involved getting in touch with pains of various kinds, emotionally as much as physically. Entering into this exploration consciously, with willingness to learn, was different than resisting pain, trying to escape from it, struggling to avoid it, and yet still suffering from it, which had made me feel like a victim. Feeling victimized felt worse than opening up to feeling vulnerable and embracing the fact of the pain.

As I felt guided from within, I engaged in what could be called "incarnating" activities, such as swimming, which involved the whole body. It was an extreme challenge, emotionally, to overcome my resistance to getting cold and wet, to expose myself to extremes of physical sensation. (However, we're not talking "extreme sports" here – just swimming in the Glen Mary Wading Pool while my son splashed around with his friends!) Within two weeks of surrendering to these incarnating activities, the right-sided pain diminished by half! Over the next two summers I worked up to swimming all the way across Echo Lake, a beautiful glacial lake in Acadia National Park. The right-sided pain still comes and goes but is not as severe as it used to be. A Lyme experienced chiropractor is helping relieve it further. Craniosacral treatments help as well.

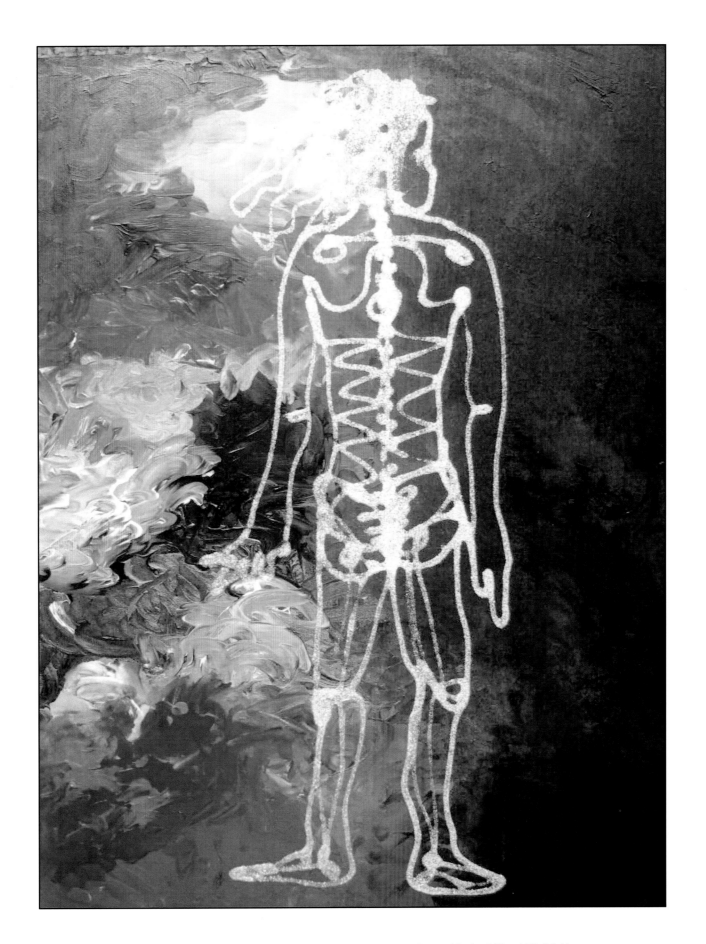

30. Standing in Both Worlds, glitter glue and acrylic on birch, 20" x 16", 2011

Another active engagement with living was scheduling lunches and teatime talks with some of my former bosses, mentors, and teachers to discuss the daunting prospect of rejoining the local workforce in some way. I also took three career aptitude tests at a career counseling office. In this way I felt that I was doing all that I could to take responsibility for myself in the world of careers and finances. Although I was taking actions to try to reestablish a professional identity, no clear answers or directions emerged for a while, partly because of the lingering need to honor my fragile health. There were no 9-5 jobs outside the home that I could fathom sustaining, and I didn't have any savings to invest in going back to college to train in another area. I applied for a grant from a foundation that helped people return to work after a long time out owing to full time parenting or illness, but I didn't qualify since I couldn't guarantee that I would be strong enough to work or attend college full time, and supporting full-time efforts was the aim of the program. I paid to get fingerprinted and registered to be a substitute teacher, making use of my training and experience as a teacher, but even part-time classroom work turned out to be too much stress, especially for the small amount of income.

As well as not finding my bearings in a professional identity, there was no strong desire to be living in my particular house or town, no sense of relying on or being embraced within a particular relationship or social group, and no particular personal goals or dreams that I felt passionate about pursuing. I couldn't re-establish the life I had before, nor plan how to concoct a new one. This "liminal zone" of uncertainly felt like floating between one lifetime and another. The energy of personal striving seemed inaccessible, even counter-productive. It felt like trying to chew harder when a tooth is coming loose, and because its roots are dissolving, it just gets wigglier! I didn't seem able to use sheer willpower to make up my mind about future goals or put a career plan into place.

Meanwhile, other transformations were taking place, outside of my rational control or understanding. Within that period of taking on incarnating activities, the "bubble" of life force energy that I sensed around and through my body made a significant shift. Instead of feeling as if it were drawn up tightly above my

ankles and not fully surrounding my feet, it seemed to fluff out and envelope all of my body and extend down below me as well. When it expanded, there was a newfound sensation of physical balance and gravity. I felt more grounded and rooted than ever before. This was not something I tried to make happen; it was an awareness that simply arrived and endured. But I'm pretty sure that facing the conflict of not wanting to be in a body made a difference.

Another interpretation of "standing in both worlds" is the idea of being "at home," consciously inhabiting, both physical and non-physical reality. Being embodied, as a human, but also being awareness, spirit, pure consciousness. Being able to be effective in ordinary daily life, while remaining conscious of being *more* than that; having a reality that *transcends* that. That's how I feel now on an average day. There was, however, quite a long period of waffling as I learned to value the subtle energetic and "spiritual" stuff in daily life.

My old life was task oriented. I judged my self-worth and success on how much I accomplished in the world. That busyness, in which I often tuned-out my inner sensing in order to accommodate unhealthy work or relationships or other conditions, could not be returned to again without becoming ill again. I learned that recovery was not to be proven by returning to my former harried busyness. I practiced letting go of feeling guilty or worrying how to rejoin the working world, and practiced honoring all the internal changes that were going on in my body, energy, heart, and mind. Not being out in the world trying to relate to very many people, nor doing requested work on someone else's time schedule, felt as essential as not disturbing a computer that is having its software updated.

In time, the perfect transitional work appeared: a part-time job ironing organic cotton sheets and pillowcases and making beds at a Bed & Breakfast within walking distance from home. The hand-made soaps and other environmentally friendly cleaning products the owners chose were safe for my chemical sensitivities, and the the atmosphere was low stress. I truly enjoyed the simplicity, predictability, and repetition of the physical labor, which afforded me the chance to stay inwardly focused as I worked behind the scenes to prepare lovely rooms for summer tourists and honeymooners. Later, that Disabilities course I mentioned earlier was offered. Out of all the courses at the college, it was the first and only one that appealed to me on a gut level. There was a clear inner sense of Yes! that I trusted.

Another unexpected opportunity was a kind offer, by my first ex-husband, of a very good deal on the house we had formerly shared. In the same town, it provided the perfect new stage-set for the next scene of my life to become clearer. Working from home would be so much easier than it had been in my own little house. This new house was an ideal space and location for tutoring and teaching art, with a separate office, a spare room to rent or meet Reiki clients in, and a double lot with flower, vegetable, and herb gardens. I never imagined I'd be given the change to live here again!

These pieces didn't come together from effortfully pushing to overcome adversity, nor from excitedly "following my passion." I was not trying to manifest a self-determined vision. I admitted and accepted that I had a limited perspective about what was possible or what aught to happen. Embracing my limits, resting in uncertainty, paying attention to my true needs, and being attentive to my gut-level awareness – such as the feeling of becoming unattached to my old home and former career and social identities – allowed my attention to be free to recognize new, highly compatible opportunities when they arose.

Lyme disease can be seen as just a hindrance that disrupts our lives and holds us back from the health we had and activities we did before. It can *also* be seen as a form of "fierce grace" that can help us peal back layers of conditioned behavior and uncover buried abilities, such as accessing (and valuing) our intuition and higher sensory perception. For me, certainly, acknowledging these buried abilities was a part of the healing process. And part of the deal with remaining in good health is to continue to acknowledge and honor this heightened sensitivity. That is not to say that a person has to become ill to obtain this "system upgrade", but I offer this positive side-effect as an idea for those who are merely seeing Lyme as a setback.

Particles and Waves

"Particles and Waves" started as a self-portrait, ink on paper, which was then ripped into pieces and strips and glued to a sky-blue board. All the pieces have spaces between them. The blue background suggests water channels or canals on a map, and teardrop shapes emerge from the paper trails. The eyes are whole and look out at the viewer. The being is conscious of its own unraveling.

Healing can involve the breakdown, surrender, and release of old habits, patterns, and images of a self that we thought we really were, which can feel like the "dissolving" of self. Going through a shattering experience, such as a tremendous loss, betrayal, accident, or serious illness, can be a way to grow a lot spiritually or psychologically in a relatively short time; compared with when life is going along "as normal," our attention can become quite focused on existential matters!

One of the scariest and most difficult conditions to endure before accepting it as part of healing was one of my most fruitful learning experiences in the long run. Back in high school, and later in the 2002-2009 era, during Lyme low points, I frequently experienced neurological disruption resulting in racing visual hallucinations. It appeared, in my mind's eye, that a movie of thousands of images was flickering past within the span of a few minutes.

Some shifts in self-perception are normal – having a certain solid sense of self or quality of "being me" that lasts for a while, then shifts gradually or because of some obvious outward influence. Moving, a change in seasons, starting a new job or grade in school, entering a new relationship, giving birth, even just seeing a movie or reading a book that touches us deeply can alter our perception of who we are and "how life is." Having a strong dream during sleep may also change our internal sense of reality such that, for a few minutes or hours after waking, the atmosphere of our self perception and normal surroundings just "feels different." The shifts in self-perception that I experienced were different than these.

During my hallucinations, each frame of the movie I witnessed seemed to be a unique and individual version of "me," with a unique feeling or tone, as if from a whole different life. The images came so quickly that it was impossible to slow them down. None of the images would stay in view long enough to allow me to sink down into "being that way" and identifying with any of them. Had any one of them endured, that would have constituted an atmosphere of "this is who I am and this is what my life is like right now." But since none of them lingered, I gathered that none of the images or feelings were truly "me," in fact "me" was more the aspect of *being* that was *witnessing* all of those images. I didn't interpret it that way back in high school, when the first episodes occurred, but by the time it happened in adulthood I had done some study of alternative healing and spirituality, so there was a different framework to relate it to. The idea that "I am not my thoughts" could be couched in the context of a spiritual practice for anyone to contemplate. But for someone with illness-induced hallucinations and racing thoughts, that idea might be a key to finding a comforting continuity that exists beyond, and in spite of, the cognitive incoherence.

After each "shattering" we go through, there may be a new reintegration. (At first it may appear to those around us that we are "coming apart at the seams"! There is no knowing how long it might take to discover some new kind of coherence that endures in spite of all the changes.) Sometimes we can pull ourselves back together. Sometimes it is more of a passive sense of *being* put back together anew. Sometimes, if we keep breathing through the intensity of being cracked and blown apart, and surrender into the unknown, we may discover a newfound freedom in remaining less "solid" than we felt before.

Now, when something happens that might have shattered "me" before, it seems to have less impact. When strong feelings arise, they tend to go right through, like a light show, as if the "substance" of self is diaphanous, rather than a solid thing that can be hit and broken. There is often a dreamlike quality to life, and an increased tendency to not take things personally. There is more serenity, less anguish. This leaves my body in a more relaxed state, which has taken a load off the immune system.

"Particles and Waves" also refers to a shift away from relying upon rationally focused "head-centered" navigation. Before the illness-enforced hiatus from my career and other active social engagement in the world, I used to think I ought to navigate most choices and decisions with mostly mental rumination, rationalizing, logically "thinking things through." I thought of the words that went through my mind as variables to be seriously weighed, and that the inner dialogues going on in there were fundamental to making good choices and decisions. When the ability to mentally focus and quickly organize thoughts and process ideas verbally got compromised during Lyme low points, I felt as if I were becoming "stupider."

As I began to recover the ability to "think straight" and focus, there was still a problem maintaining motivation. Obviously physical fatigue played a role, including a certain brand of fatigue that comes from enduring pain for a long time. But even when much of the physical pain resolved and I was regularly getting more sleep, there was still a noticeable lack of ability to sustain mentally conceived plans or self-conceived projects. I mostly went through the motions of doing what needed to be done each day to maintain my household and meet my children's needs. I could still make common-sense choices, such as buying healthy food, and maintain responsible routines, such as preparing meals on time. But there was little inner drive to accomplish anything, even activities that used to seem personally fulfilling, such as writing and painting. What motivation there was usually dissolved very quickly. Feeling "stupid" got replaced by feeling "lazy" – except that I was always fairly engaged in some activity or another.

During the daytime, while my children were in school, I spent many hours reading about other people's spiritual and psychological "awakening" experiences. Even though there was no practical, rational, or financially beneficial reason to do so, there was a warm *heartfelt* motivation to explore this – and a *gut* level draw – an *appetite*. It felt important, and easy. I discovered evidence that some of what I was going through could be seen not just as symptoms of illness, but also as symptoms of awakening. I learned that it is common for many people to go through a gradual or sudden dropping away of

31. Particles and Waves, paper, ink, glitter, and acrylic on birch, 20" x 16", 2011

personal will. This phenomenon is easier to recognize after it happens. It's not something one makes happen. Whatever energy generated it before just isn't there to support it. Whenever I looked at my low motivation to make plans and strive toward self-determined goals as a negative symptom of illness, I felt disempowered. When I began to consider that my lack of personal will could actually be a phase of awakening, I felt at ease and serene. I learned that sooner or later another way of operating comes into play: a feeling of being in the flow of a more universal will.

One of my "life coaches," via her books and the internet, was Byron Katie, who teaches a practice called "The Work." It is a process of inquiry in which you question thoughts to see if they are true. A thought arises, seeming to be true. Inquiry involves asking, "Is it true? Do I really know that it is true? How might I feel if I didn't hold this belief? Turn it around—could the opposite also be just as true?" After a fair amount of conscious inquiry, I experienced a period of several weeks of spontaneous rapid mental activity which could be described as the matching of each arising thought with its opposite, such that it was apparent that none of the thoughts were *fundamentally* true. All were just *relative* truths, with *relative* value based on their context or from a particular perspective.

I seemed to literally feel the canceling out taking place in my brain, like a visceral rewiring. Ideas meeting their match, particles and anti-particles colliding and dissolving into nothing. There was a sensation in the brain of barriers breaking down, for the only thing that separated a thought from its opposite was a "fence" put up around that little area, cordoning it off to keep that idea surrounded by all its supporting evidence and keeping out anything that would reveal it as only relatively true. Each "fence" had been constructed from fear, so as the fences were deconstructed there was often an accompanying sensation of facing some fear in order to acknowledge, that, "Well... yes, this 'truth' or 'fact' could be seen in another light." The task of trying to strongly "believe in" anything seemed like trying to keep shoring up a straw house on a windy day. All beliefs were seen as mental creations, constructed stories, rather than fundamental truths. They often

required conscious (and laborious) maintenance by keeping tabs on what other thoughts or ideas or facts were allowed to associate with them. Even the entity called a "self" was revealed as only a mental construction. A whole different sense of self might be constructed based on what beliefs were included in the package. I spent hours staring into space observing each thought meet its opposite and "pop" into nothing, leaving a sensation of vast stillness and silence.

Often the inner dialogue of one idea facing off with another ended with "Gosh. I don't know. I don't *really* know." Getting used to residing in this psychological state of blankness or "not-knowing" went against the grain of all my formal education, but it was a relief from the battering of internal mental arguments, judgements, assessments, comparisons, and clever theorizing that had no end. Now the process of inquiry is often so quick that it involves no writing or imaginary dialogues; there is just a recognition, when a thought arises that seems to be vying for supremacy, that its opposite is inevitably somewhere in there with it; so the bubble pops and once again there is silence in the place of what would have been the beginning of another internal mental argument.

Sometimes watching thoughts is like floating above a room watching people arguing or chatting at a party. Calm and clarity is found in sensing the quiet spacious presence of the room, rather than trying to make sense of the mental chatter. Serenity is not from making the thoughts go away or be quiet, but rather by shifting attention to the silence that enfolds them.

It is no longer possible for me to experience clarity or certainty if I look at choices and decisions from just a mental awareness. The mental level of perception has been revealed as dualistic. On a practical level, this change renders old problem solving methods such as writing a list of pros and cons no longer useful; it is just a matter of time before the dominant side of the list may be counterbalanced by the other, *ad infinitum*. Every answer would have to be qualified, and none would ever win as ultimately "correct." No absolute answers of "right" and "wrong" can be generated from that level of perception, no matter how hard I might try.

What takes the place of trying to mentally work things out by thinking hard about them is just being quietly attentive. Listening to the silence that underlies the specific mental chatter is what soft focus peripheral vision is to staring. By giving attention to just being quietly attentive, and hanging out in not-knowing, my mind becomes clear and available. Then insights, invitations, visions of possibilities, and opportunities arise. There's not a sense of me personally pushing or straining to figure something out, rather there's a sense of being present, observing what awareness emerges. When there seem to be decisions and choices, I include other "feeling centers" to help me navigate: the heart and the gut. Usually there is a felt sense of what would be compatible, such as a warm glowing feeling, a pleasant shiver up the spine, or a sensation of resonance. In day-to-day ordinary reality, there is often a feeling of "just knowing," in the moment, what to do, without much effort to figure things out. Instead of a focused beam of attention, it's more of a surrounding field, kind of like "having eyes in the back of your head." There may also be a sense of seeing into the future that is as natural as one might see into the physical distance. "Another car is about to tear around the corner into this parking lot, so don't back up yet. There it comes. Now drive home." Without effort or fear there is just clarity.

Heart Opening

Lyme can damage the heart tissue and mess with the heart beat – I used to frequently have both racing palpitations and random pauses. For years I felt a general sense of physical strain in the heart area; a heavy, squeezed, tired heart. Pushing myself physically, such as running or swimming or lifting heavy objects, could quickly result in heart palpitations, trembling hands, feeling fatigued, and particularly strained in the chest. I felt the need to guard my heart from exertion, sensing that being strained would damage it. When I purposely focused attention on my heart, there tended to be a lot of emotional pain there, as well, particularly a homesick longing. Along with and following the transformations I felt in my head, I had a general goal of wanting to "heal my heart," both literally and metaphorically.

Much new research is coming out about the powerful healing forces of the heart. It emits an electromagnetic field that is thousands of times more powerful than that of the brain. Simply putting your hand over your heart, touching your chest, releases hormones that help you feel good. Visualizing "dropping into the heart" and "looking" out from that place in your body is one way to place attention on this heart-field, which invites the rest of the body's organs to entrain with that organizing field.

During a meditation on "dropping awareness into the heart," I saw a vision of my heart as a marvelous Jain temple I had actually visited in India. It had stupendous pillars supporting an intricately filigreed ceiling resembling lace, all carved out of white marble. But in my "heart temple" all the surfaces appeared to be coated with black soot. I wondered what the "soot" was. Many memories, recent and old, came tumbling into awareness. A lifetime of suppressed grief had apparently come due for processing. Sadness, grief, longing, loneliness, and other feelings began to emerge into my conscious awareness. As they were accepted instead of denied, a new resilience grew. Standing in the fire of strong feelings and allowing them to be felt led to being less fazed by new experiences, able to feel deeply open in the heart more of the time, under more circumstances. It wasn't that I got rid of so-called negative feelings and then was left with the so-called positive feelings. It was more of an increased capacity to inhabit heart-centered awareness regardless of what feelings arose. There could also be awareness of sad events and the suffering of other people, animals, and the planet without freaking out and shutting down into defense or taking it personally and then becoming angry, dejected, or depressed.

With Buddhist teacher Pema Chödrön as one of my guides, I discovered a meditation called *tonglen*. It involves breathing in pain and suffering, and breathing out peace or whatever else you imagine as healing. You can start with your own specific suffering, and then remember that there are other people going through the same circumstances, so you do *tonglen* for everyone's sake. In the process you may find that you are opening up to feeling a sense of connection, solidarity, and

32. Heart Opening
charcoal and acrylic on canvas
10" x 10", 2011

compassion. The compassionate heart embraces both the world's suffering and the individual's suffering.

I could not seem to manufacture a felt sense of peace, love and joy in the small space of time between the "in" breath and the "out" breath, I could only generate the wording, not the feeling. There were some modifications of the *tonglen* meditation which I found to be quite useful. If you want to try, here are a few tips: First, don't envision that little you is sucking all that crap, like pollution, into your own physical body, nor suffer the delusion that you, as a person, must absorb and purify the woes of the world, as a martyr being sacrificed. Rather, envision the heart as a doorway. Whatever fear or pressure or worry comes up to it, imagine the heart breathing it in, accepting it fully. Except that instead of the heart being a little chambered room inside your body, imagine that it is a doorway into a space that is infinitely large and wise and capable of handling anything. Sometimes I saw it as a deep black velvet space as vast as the night sky. Then, whatever gets breathed in goes right *through* your own heart doorway into that space. You don't need to understand that space or what it is doing, just know that nothing fazes it, everything is welcome, and trust that it will prepare the perfect remedy or response to whatever it takes in. You don't need to figure out what that might be. You are not personally responsible for mentally conjuring up the antidote. You simply breath out, and *whatever that mystery is* that is needed and healing to all is what is breathed out. "You" as an individual are not "doing" anything except breathing in and out. You're not feeling-sorry-for, not planning-how-to-fix, not struggling-to-understand, not seeing-where-this-is-going. You are simply offering your little individual self as a gateway between worlds. As soon as I welcome whatever seems broken and unhealed by breathing it in, there is no more emotional pressure or worry or fear. The crap of the world goes in. The blessing and peace of the infinite comes out. Basically, the little self serves a perfect healing function by being a hole-in-the-wall; by being nothing! This can be done while driving in a car, walking a dog, washing dishes, lying in bed; it doesn't require remembering words, nor does it need to be done sitting cross-legged on a fancy cushion for a specified length of time.

Tonglen is a wonderful antidote to one of the most common New Age misunderstandings. The idea of focusing on positive thoughts and the idea that we will "manifest" what we focus upon has often been overly simplified. There is fear that if we allow ourselves to look at what is unhealed and feel the pain, we will somehow manifest *more* pain and suffering. This sets up a cycle of a repression and denial of that which could actually be healed if it were allowed to arise into our conscious awareness! This myth also reinforces our illusion of separation and the belief that we must maintain that in order to stay safe. If I am trying to avoid focusing on pain and suffering, I might treat someone else's pain and suffering as a personal threat. Defending the fortress of my own little separate energy bubble, trying to keep it from becoming "contaminated" from the "bad vibes" that are "out there in the world" (or in my client, if I'm a healer) fortifies the belief that the individual self must stay walled-off from everything else in order to be well. This is only *conditional* well-being. Becoming willing to "breathe in" whatever I am aware of, instead of defending myself from it, fostered a sense of compassion and unity with all that is. It gave "little me" a way to "be with" any feeling that came up and not be dragged down into fear, denial, and resistance. In my imagination, the heart can also seem to be a giant virtual "room" where I can sense an immediate connection with anyone I happen to think of.

As well as practicing *tonglen*, there was also a sense of being drawn into a process of physical and energetic transformation that had a momentum of its own, which I could resist or surrender into, rather than direct. It seemed best to let whatever was happening to run its course, to simply allow it and not resist. In prior years, there had been moments when I felt as if an enormous magnet were pulling on my heart. This heart-pull was visceral. It came and went on its own. There seemed to be a lot of energy in that area of the body, and frequently energy came racing into my feet, then into my legs and through other parts of my body. For the better part of several months in 2011-2012, during the time of focusing on *tonglen* and clearing the "temple" of my heart, as I'd envisioned it, I often felt as if my heart were a white fire. I imagined this clear flame was burning out the inside of my chest so that it was becoming hollowed out inside. The energy felt like electricity of a very fine and subtle nature. I imagined that it was lighting up and burning off congestion, cleaning up cells, super-charging them and leaving them free of toxins and disease. Sometimes my heart and chest area physically ached as if a hole were being burned open in my chest or as if hands were literally pulling apart a gap in my chest, making it bigger. It felt like a physical, energetic, and psychological heart-ache and expansion. Sometimes this became so fierce that I felt as if the very fiber of my being was dissolving into nothing. Very strong feelings of agony and ecstasy were also apparent at times, as if testing an electrical system to see how much voltage it could sustain without shorting out. Nothing serious showed up during the times I wore a heart monitor.

The closest I came to portraying this phase was to render a minimal charcoal sketch in canvas, a self portrait seated in lotus position. I used a candle to burn a hole through the heart area, healed the edges with acrylic paint, and painted white "light rays" coming out from the hole. This "heart-purification" settled down after a while, and now the energy there usually feels calm and quiet. Sometimes it seems as if a sweet white waterfall of light is flowing through my heart and showering over my body and out into the world. I no longer feel any concern about the physical health of my heart.

Memorial with Rose Petals

I've heard from many people who are still mired in debilitating symptoms from Lyme, and others who are farther along with their recovery. Some feel heartened to be making even a little progress, while others are deeply frustrated by the lack of it. In general, those who are making progress are open – or learning to be open – to making changes in their lives, as well as learning to surrender to having their lives *be* changed. Acceptance of change – and active and passive participation in it – or resistance to change, seem to be key elements in the equation. Those who are feeling stuck, stalled at a plateau, or resigned to the idea that they will always be as ill as they are, usually display some characteristics of holding on tightly to some aspect of their identity, their world view, their accepted

reality. Part of this is feeling like a victim, and strong feelings of resentment toward someone else or some situation. Usually it is not a mystery who the villains are, for the persons are likely to volunteer their story. With others it can be a more subtle gesture, such as carrying around a photo album of dead pets in one's purse, and each viewing and sharing reinforces a story of longing, loss, and attachment to the past. All of this is part of what makes us human, not a mistake, but when one's body is very ill every little stress just adds to the burden. Grieving, releasing the past, practicing forgiveness, and letting go of focusing on stories about the ways we have been wounded or "the way life should have been" can be very important influences on our physical healing.

Some of the losses that I experienced in recent years paralleled losses that I was "valiantly enduring" by suppressing feelings of grief in the summer of 1984, which happens to be when I first contracted Lyme! The grief involved the loss of special relationships and feeling abandoned. I wonder if my immune response would have been any different that summer if I had been more vibrant instead of trying to appear strong by shutting down emotionally? That's not to imply that people who are happy and "well adjusted" will not get chronic Lyme. Many people, especially children, are in the prime of their lives when they become infected. Highly fit professional athletes, avid hikers, gardeners, children playing happily outdoors, may be brought down by Lyme no matter how healthy their attitudes are at the time.

It is not really useful second-guessing what might have happened "if only;" it's more practical to reconcile what did. Arguing with the past is a form of distraction. The urge to avoid the present moment and stay numb or distracted can be a reflexive act of self-preservation, but it doesn't serve our health if it becomes habitual. Reinforcing the dramas of our victimhood, woundedness, regrets, and angry judgements cause emotional and energetic stagnation, which impedes our physical healing. One of the least helpful comments a person can say to one who is ill is, "This should not be happening to you." Though seemingly sympathetic, such comments may drive the stake of victimhood deeper into the ground.

33. Memorial with Rose Petals
acrylic, paper, glue, and rose water on birch
16" x 20", 2011

In the beginning, practicing acceptance of this moment, and "living in the present" does require courage. Acceptance is not the same as putting on rose-tinted glasses. Really inhabiting and embodying present-time awareness can mean facing very strong feelings. Numbness melts into sensation. But if one stays with the process, buried feelings from events in the past can be digested and assimilated by experiencing them in the present. This can release the drag on our current-time body chemistry – and thus on our immune system functioning. We can invent our own rituals to do this. I did this through crying (which releases toxins from the body), writing, and art projects.

"Memorial With Rose Petals" was a process piece that took weeks to finish. First I drew simple cartoon images that referred to specific memories and people involved, then I collaged the images onto the base board and stood it up where I could see it. The feelings of sadness and loss were still quite raw. Then I painted other sheets of paper in different rose colors, and tore hundreds of paper "rose petals" from them. Roses were something one might scatter at a funeral or a wedding. In the Jain temple in India, women left offerings of rose petals and mint leaves. The scent of roses also related to a specific loss I was grieving, so I mixed rose water into the glue. Every day I glued a few petals over the collage. This took a few weeks. It wasn't forced. There had to be an honest willingness to let go a little more, to say good-bye. The making of the art was a ritual of letting go. Now I look at it and feel no pathos. Regarding those stories, I feel cleared out of grief and resentment. There is neutrality, acceptance, and gratitude.

As assimilation and integration of feelings that were denied and held at bay takes place, the whole system becomes more integrated. Eventually, present-moment awareness is truly felt to be the simplest way to live. The most freedom is living *just now, just this.* As the excavation process goes on, there can also be buried treasures that come forth into the light of conscious awareness: deeper feelings of love, appreciation, beauty, and memories of dear experiences to be cherished.

In this world of dualities, life can also give as unexpectedly and completely as it takes away. If you are not fixated on what you have lost, not convinced that you are doomed to live as a victim, then you can be open to the magic of new possibilities when they are offered. There is much about the way my life is now that I would never have thought to ask for. If I had been trying to manifest certain fantasies, I wouldn't have even contemplated some of the best aspects of my current life. It's simply way better than I ever hoped for. I didn't get here through planning. Most of the best of what's happening came about "out of the blue." If I ever had anything to do with it, it was having an open heart at the time of being shown each new possibility, so that I could recognize the generosity, the potential for compatibility, and the love that was being offered.

One example is to be playing music again. At Interlochen, I had a fabulous clarinet, but I sold it during the same period of time in which I gave away my art supplies. Buying a new instrument and taking up music again was not on my agenda. That element of life seemed permanently over. Then, a couple of years ago, life landed a fine old clarinet in my lap. Also a full size and three-quarter size viola, and a very nice upright piano! All for free! These unsolicited gifts were not lost on me. It was pretty obvious that Life was putting music back into my home. My daughter took up piano, my son took up viola, and a new friend spent about a month of free time overhauling that clarinet (for free), so it very well had to be played.

Woodwinds require fine muscle control in the mouth. One's embouchure gets weak without daily practice. So it took a while before I could play more than a few minutes. Any amount of practicing felt therapeutic. It made me breathe deeply, required hand coordination, and challenged my brain to read music. I got out a beginner book and started on page one. It seemed that it would take a long time to recover much ability. Then, one day, I got out a solo that I'd worked on with the help of my favorite teacher, thirty years before. His pencil marks were on the pages. As I began playing through that piece, a section of my memory became reactivated. Suddenly I remembered how to make the tone quality round and how to play not just notes but music. An ability I thought I'd lost came back out to play! For many years I'd had reoccurring nightmares of showing up for a music rehearsal unprepared.

When I was getting back in shape, I dreamed that I walked into a group of musicians, sat down at the end of the row, and smiled, happy to be there, even without being prepared. That same month College of the Atlantic's student orchestra was opened up to the community. So I joined! It is a marvelous experience to play with strings, woodwinds, brass, and percussion, to be bathed in a sensual sea of sounds.

Healing Within a Lotus

Concurrently and after the dominant "healing in the heart" phase, my attention was drawn downward into the belly. An intuitive energy healer was instrumental in giving me support and feedback during some intense exploration of what information was lurking down there. Often, during a hands-on healing session, I would drift into a light sleep and see images in my imagination. Meanwhile, she would also see images, some that meant nothing to her, personally, but she would write notes. Then we would share what we'd seen, and it was remarkable how much similarity there was. Often the images meant something symbolically significant. I highly recommend consulting with a reputable medical intuitive as an ally to help confirm your own intuitive awareness. It is like having a music lesson with a trained teacher who can offer a "tuning fork" by affirming that you are "onto something" when you may feel uncertain what to listen for on your own. As I experienced it, medical intuitives did not usually tell me anything I didn't already know, but hearing them confirmed it and made me more confident about what I was picking up on my own. I'd feel a resonance of "yes!" in the solar plexus, and then on my own I could tap into that sensation and trust my own intuition more.

During those sessions there was often a correlation between the imagined stories and an actual physical change. For example, in the beginning there was a tightly wound sensation of resistance in my abdomen, and a blankness or numbness, as if the intelligence of that feeling center had been ignored so long that the screen had gone dark or blank like a computer left alone. Giving attention to that area was like waking up the screen. I also became aware of a physical sensation of warmth and well-being, like a tiny flame that was barely a flicker, but

which grew steadily larger with attention. Also, there was a dark, shrouded, discordant quality to some energy in the abdomen – but when I opened my vision to "see" what was around me, it was as if I were being held within a giant healing presence that accepted and absorbed all the discord. "Healing Within a Lotus" was one attempt to picture that impression. I discovered that there was such joy available in resting in that sweet surrounding presence. I didn't have to heal myself *first*, or earn it, or create it with my intention. It was already there. Between that, and the energetic grounding, and the opening of the heart, there was a sense of having found an oasis of well-being which grew from being a very tiny place to stand on tiptoe, into a larger realm in which I could fully relax.

The Tree of Trauma and Fear

Sometimes uncomfortable feelings signal the need for concrete changes, and one must summon the courage and willpower to take action – maybe to try something new and challenging. At times the gesture that is the most authentic may be to try to "move the energy" by expressing it in some safe and appropriate manner, such as talking it out, writing it out, crying it out, or dancing it out. One may try to uplift one's mood or "vibration" by reading something inspirational, going for a walk in the woods, playing soothing music, "tapping" on the body along meridians to release tension and "balance" the energy. One may consciously invoke ideas that may help one find a broader perspective, such as, "This is an illusion," or "This, too, shall pass." Once the uncomfortable "energy" feels "cleared" one may feel temporarily relieved.

Having applied those tactics aplenty, I did not understand why, after seeming to make a lot of progress cultivating inner peace and well-being, in early 2012 there seemed to be a sort of downward inflationary spiral going on. For some reason, the process up lightening up seemed to not only stall but go into reverse. I seemed less able to neutralize inner discomfort; the inner condition of anxiety intensified. On the outside, my life was running smoothly. Technically I was "safe". There were no new traumatizing situations playing out. There was minimal conflict within my family relationships – in fact, there was more

34. Healing within a Lotus
acrylic on birch
16" x 16", 2011

harmony with everyone than ever before. I had a fairly neutral relationship with the world in general, a fairly routine daily schedule, and my basic survival needs were being met. Inside, however, there was so much struggle – I could hardly stand to wake up and still be me! There was such heaviness. I would wake in the morning and think, "Oh, God, *this* still?" During the night I often woke with a pounding heart and high anxiety. I couldn't understand why an underlying drone of angst seemed to be stuck on LOUD all the time. The fact that the outer life was so harmonious made the perfect foil to realize that the conflict was being generated from within.

My life inside felt like the scene in a movie where the protagonist is being chased through a dark woods or alley, and no matter how fast she runs, the predator is gaining on her. In spite of presenting to the world as being a well-balanced person who was confident and responsible, I felt hounded by fear inside. Fear was breathing down my neck. I felt as if I were inside a maze that had no exit; life was a constant journey of "Seek – but do not find." There was fear about environmental hazards beyond my ability to control. There were things I wanted to change about myself and my life that I didn't seem to have any ability to improve beyond a certain point. It perplexed me that any plans for concrete change that I was trying to set in motion just didn't gel; it seemed as if there wasn't enough energy behind them, or the timing was off; or something else – out of my control – was holding the brake pedal down. All the time it felt as if I were trying to drive forward with the brakes on, and I didn't seem to be able to get them to loosen up. The only thing I had not tried was "stopping". Stopping meant stopping all trying to get away from the fear, letting fear completely catch up with me. Giving up. Being defeated. No more resistance. Surrender! Ah ha! That awful idea seemed the most authentic of all. Thus began a new experiment.

Surrendering to fear is not the same as panicking and acting out of control. It actually involves immense presence. It is like doing inner shadow-dancing, precise inner *meeting* of fear on a moment-by-moment basis. This often amounted to being willing to "sit still" (psychologically speaking, in terms of focus, not literally sitting) in the midst of feeling whatever strong

feelings of fear came upon me, as they presented themselves to the most extreme degree, without doing anything to try to control or numb them, such as going to sleep, or playing soothing music and other New-Age pain killers. This also involved a surrender of mental negotiations, a letting go of inner arguments, rationalizations, and mental manipulations, just being very present and intimate with the fear non-verbally. Allowing what I had been avoiding most of all to come right up and sit down next to me... not flinching as it moved even closer... not spacing-out or drawing away as it completely inhabited the space I was still defining as "mine", not avoiding contact as it permeated every cell. Allowing fear, pain, hopelessness, defeat, and all other conditions of suffering to just be, without trying to change them one iota. As counter-intuitive as this seemed, it felt very compelling. There was a willingness to try that, to allow that. I couldn't explain it to anyone at the time, it just would have sounded like giving up in a resigned, dejected way. It actually involved a lot of strength, and it felt like the authentic thing to do. I didn't know what the outcome would be. I could not see where it was going. There was no way to anticipate anything about it. There was no outcome I was shooting for, except to keep surrendering indefinitely. Whatever fear or uncomfortable feeling came up, I stopped trying to control it, change it, or get away from it. I did that with everything that came up, for as long as it came up. Each day felt very long. Throughout this phase normal daily life continued on the outside.

The concept of stopping was applied to many specific internal projects: Stopping looking in the past for explanations of why things had "gone wrong." Stopping revising the stories about the past in order to create a narrative that I liked better, that explained all the losses and defeats and pointed toward more success in the future. Stopping all the planning for how my life could become better, or how, if my health, character, and abilities could be improved, maybe things would go more the way I wanted them to. Giving up on hoping for better health. Giving up on hoping to be in a long-term healthy loving relationship. Giving up any and all ideas of a future that I had been holding onto. Stopping all hoping for my life or self to be different. Accepting that I could not seem to develop it any

35. Tree of Trauma and Fear
charcoal on paper
12" x 18", 2012

farther. Accepting the feeling of being defeated. In spiritual terms, stopping could be called the death of all seeking.

One night, later that winter, I dreamed of a black tree the size of a giant sequoia, representing a tree that was ancient, beyond one human life span. It was swaying. I thought it might come down on me, but that didn't matter. I felt no fear. Dying was not a problem. There was full acceptance of whatever was happening. Then the tree fell away from me. I used it as a bridge to walk over the scrubby underbrush, out of the woods. There were no roots. They had been dissolved. So it had to fall; nothing was supporting it. When I awoke I sketched this.

About a week later, as I was laying on the massage table (fully clothed), the intuitive energy healer was scanning her hands over my body, sensing the energy of organs and chakras and whatever else she was paying attention to. Without having heard about my tree dream, she had a vision of a tree falling – almost onto my body, then falling away instead. She wrote "trauma tree" in her notes. It was also a metaphor, to her, of illness. The trunk of the trauma tree branched out into all manner of specific expressions of major and minor traumas that I had experienced, including Lyme.

In light of the dramatic image of a tree almost falling on me she was surprised, scanning my body and energy, that she was not picking up any fear or trauma "vibes" in the gut area. I laughed at the affirmation. No, there had not been any for a while. I realized then that the dream was the message, "the war is over," and the vision she was picking up was more of an acknowledgement of something that had already happened than of a current event. After she shared her vision, I described my dream. We were mutually delighted! I had been calling it the "tree of fear." Maybe letting go of all resistance to fear had something to do with dissolving those roots?

For many months after that dream, the project of managing high anxiety was over. In its absence there was a quiet serenity that took some getting used to – like the ringing in your ears when a loud droning noise finally stops and there is a period of adjusting to the quiet. Or when you get out of a car after a very

long time on the freeway, and for a while your body sort of sloshes forward a bit until it adjusts to being still. Compared with angst this serenity seemed almost boring!

Soon after that session I went to my doctor and proposed getting off all medicines. Recently we had discussed that I had "plateaued" as far as not noting any more improvement from taking medicine – that had been one of the things I had feared, that medicine would not make me any better. We agreed to give it a go, with the clause that I could go back on for a while if I regressed. But inside I felt intuitively that a shift had occurred and I simply would not be needing them.

Eye into Nothing

"Eye into Nothing" began as a blob of black paint in the middle of white, spread out with my fingers instead of a brush. It morphed into a giant eye with no iris, as if the eye opened into a vast dark void. I first discovered how to access and find "shelter" in this void while in the midst of neurological Lyme symptoms.

Sensory-overload: not being able to turn off the internal chatter and electrical buzzing sensations or deactivate my mind's fixation on incoming stimulation brought me into the realm of insanity. Except that I was fortunate enough to be in touch with some aspect of intelligent consciousness that was aware of all of this without being captured by it. When I felt most overwhelmed (lights too bright, sounds too loud, ideas too flurrying, impressions accumulating similar to after-images when you've look at a bright light) I would often take refuge in a quiet room or warm bath, and lie there facing the wall with an unfocused gaze. Unable to mentally manufacture a pleasant image or call up a pleasant memory, unable to focus on any images at all, I learned to drop into the chaos, surrender into the uncontrollability of the sensory barrage, and somehow arrive in a space or inner condition that I called "the center of the center of everything." Paradoxically, this was also a place of blessed nothingness. I could rest there – in nothing – as pure awareness. It turns out that Lyme was a catalyst for me to discover deep states of meditative calm. In as much as Lyme

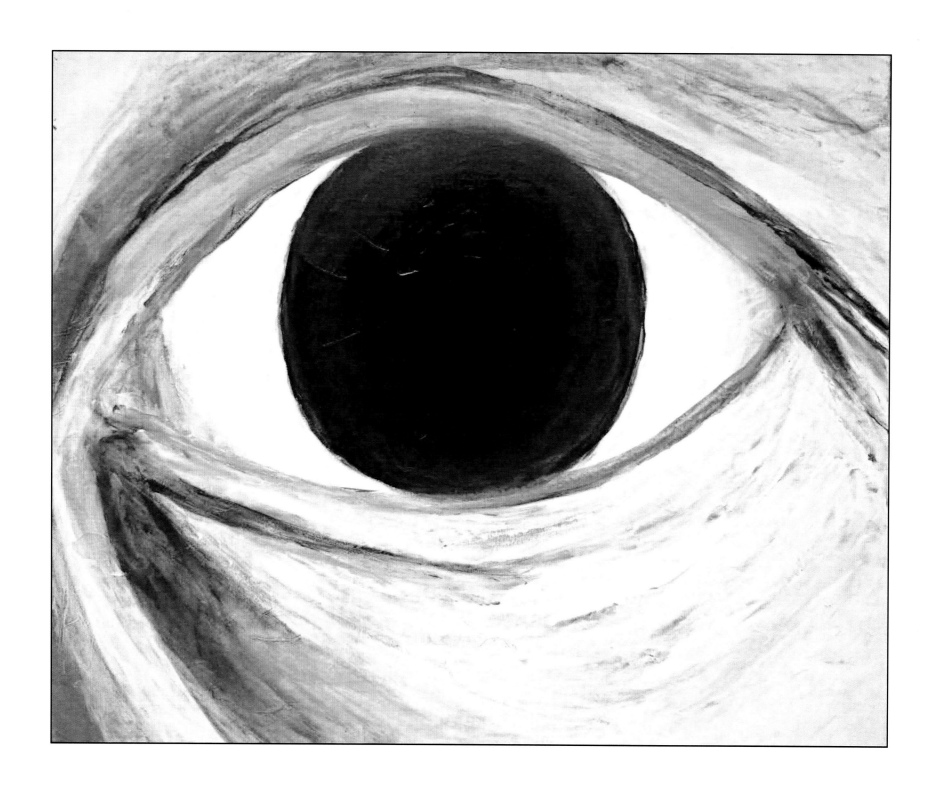

36. Eye into Nothing
acrylic on birch
16" x 20", 2011

caused neurological hurricanes, by default there was also an eye in the storm. While I was most ill I got lots of practice in finding that "centerless center," resting within that "groundless ground." This comes in handy now, in ordinary daily life. Whenever I notice that I'm getting caught up in worrying, or when answers to problems are not forthcoming, when the "particulars" of life just seem to be too much to sort out, I can drop into that absolute stillness and silence, and then rest.

Another awareness that became apparent through having Lyme was a quality of transcending the individual body or self. Being a specific ill person enduring whole-body physical pain just felt like too much to endure at times. The pain was so complete that there was nothing but pain – pain in every joint and muscle, pain in the bones, a burning sensation in the spine and head. There was no relief in the physical realm, no escape at the level of physical reality. Uncertain when or if this would end, there was incentive to stop identifying as being only that individual body. There was much incentive to do inquiry into the nature of reality, and a willingness, an urgency, to open up to being something more, something beyond that which was suffering so profoundly. There was a ripening of willingness to let go of defining myself as just this biological entity, especially when I learned that our bodies are really more like a planet, colonized by many pounds of non-human microorganisms! What I was calling "me" shifted from "this body" and "these feelings and thoughts" to include "the *awareness* of all this."

Many people describe heightened anxiety from Lyme. I learned to recognize that many of my fits of anxiety had no basis in outer reality: the anxiety came on first and *then* the mind went looking for reasons. The effect of seeming to be pushed, by illness, to the edge of my tolerance and then over the edge, was surprisingly positive. It knocked me out of the familiar identity of being a particular island or person beset with particular problems, drowning in drama, right off the edge into the ocean. The moments of experiencing this ocean were vacations from all struggling.

After the tree dream, there were several continuous months of sustained "oceanic awareness." It went from being an

occasional fleeting visit to an extended living experience. The little island of "me" still had her ups and downs, but I also experienced that "I" was the vast sea of consciousness around her. All that was "not me" was also "me"; and on the other hand there was a selfless quality to that vast nothingness or infinite spaciousness that hosts all feelings, forms, and phenomena. It was that which is changeless no matter how much change seems to transpire within it. That which does change – thoughts, feelings, and the world of form – seemed quite insubstantial by comparison.

For months after the "tree of trauma and fear" fell, calmness and neutrality were the norm. The neutrality was equal in both directions: things didn't bug me as much, but for the most part things also didn't "make me happy" anymore. It was clear that nothing ever really did; it was an illusion that anything could really *make* the individual happy. Compared with before, there was no longer much missing or anticipation of anything. I could still play this game, but mostly just being present with what was happening was the easiest way to be. I laughed much more. A new version of happiness sprouted up: I would be doing something that once would have seemed serious, but it was no longer perceived as a problem – such as when the wind blew out the plexiglass window on the porch and it cracked all over the road. Picking up the pieces was just picking up the pieces, with a goofy smile on my face, amused about how unfazed I felt. There was no heavy weight of "dealing with a problem;" there was just sunlight and wind and grass and plastic and bending over and wondering at the strange physics that got that window to blow out instead of in.

Sometimes all of a sudden I would get a little wiggly feeling in the solar plexus that I used to associate with the delight of being "in love." It sometimes surprised me because of the lack of logic - it seemed causeless. The "all is well" feeling just blossomed up out of nowhere, with no obvious trigger for it to happen right then. This was not a totally new experience; it used to happen at other times in my life. But the feeling of openness would soon collapse back down into contraction, and my normally serious personality would preside. After the tree fell, the ratios were reversed. The serenity had nothing to do with the little Emily character altering her behavior to become a more laid-back personality. I could only fake that on the outside, never on the inside! Calm became the new ordinary flavor. Unconditional well-being was a nice lens to be wearing, for it tended to put into focus that which was ready to be celebrated. It tended to make it easier to recognize possibilities to dance gracefully with whatever was arising instead of feeling serious, confronted, or offended – dancing with possibilities, instead of navigating by attraction and aversion. This was not the same as "feeling better" physically, it was on a different level. However, since the central nervous system was no longer subject to a perpetual vibration of anxiety, this transformation precipitated some welcome changes in health.

The "lightening up" that I experienced was not a permanent shift out of egoic (separate self) consciousness, but it was a wonderful vacation from the heaviness of selfhood and all its dramas, struggles, and perceptions of suffering. Now the little Emily character still goes through her motions of daily living, and things might happen to her body, but often there is a sense of being in and around and through her, being the space in which the play-acting of her character's role and other's roles appear to be playing out. The whole world, which seemed so formidable before, often feels like a vivid dream. Even when I have re-identified as being the anxious serious suffering self, it has seemed like a little ice cube in a warm sea of tranquil awareness. Some of its anxiety comes from the anticipation of its own "demise". Overall, the balance has swung toward embracing and accepting life as it unfolds. Embracing uncertainty instead of lamenting my lack of control. Accepting whatever is happening NOW is the key to peace. This doesn't mean that I am not moved to do anything to make the world a better place. It means operating from a perspective that even more effectively aligns my individual self with the rest of the world. Acceptance *is* the entry point into awareness that transcends suffering. With that attitude, the individual self feels uplinked to a vast field of loving intelligence which plays through it, and as it. I take heart that I can continue to choose to practice resting in and as that. The painting "Eye into Nothing" is a celebration of this awareness.

Cloister Walk

The painting and collage "Cloister Walk" was inspired by a hiking trail near my home where I often walked in silent contemplation. I included it in this book partly to show how different the healing artwork was from my typical landscapes. It was created two years before I learned that I had Lyme. In a way it foreshadowed the journey I would soon embark upon.

The outward path of healing may involve and affect many people: our family, friends, doctors, and other healers. We might have a *sangha* of special friends with whom we are intimately connected, who offer their wisdom, humor, and encouragement. Our healing community may even be global, a community of people who are going through the same illness or environmental challenges. But inwardly, the path of healing is a very personal journey that we each must make ourselves. When it comes down to it, healing, as with a spiritual journey, is nobody's business but your own. People may offer examples, suggestions, and inspiration, but no one else really knows what is best or right for you.

To turn the tables for a minute, perhaps you are the one who is well, and you know of someone who is ill, and you have ideas for what he or she should do to heal. It is healthy to want to help. Offering ideas about methods of healing you have tried, or helping with chores, is a fine thing to do. If someone invites you to participate in his or her healing process, such as asking you to help cook meals or drive to appointments, by all means feel welcome to say yes. But notice if you feel personally invested in getting someone else to heal in any particular way. Look at your role as helper and make sure you are respectfully agreeing to support that person in a way not forced by you.

Healing may involve a great deal of inner psychological or spiritual work. It is up to each individual when (and if) that person is willing and ready to enter this process. It really doesn't matter how much knowledge you have. You might be a walking encyclopedia about various methods of healing. You might be on the cutting edge of research involved in treating that person's ailment. But even if the person has that exact

37. Cloister Walk
watercolor, oil pastel, birch bark, gold leaf,
collage papers, 26.75" x 34.5", 2007

illness, and you would perform the treatment at no cost, it is still up to that person to decide if and when he or she is ready and available to participate in healing. If you are not in someone else's shoes, you really cannot anticipate what that person will encounter in the healing process, even if you seem to have healed from the "same" illness. Humility before everyone else's healing journey, and getting on with your own, is the way to go.

Some aspects of healing may not make sense unless you are going through them. Conventional wisdom and some popular beliefs about how healing works point in the direction of putting effort into a "positive attitude" and cultivating a "fighting spirit." Illness brought me to some plateaus and dead ends in which the rules of how life worked seemed to have changed. I could not always produce desired changes through hoping and planning and trying to make improvements through personal willpower. I discovered new strength from facing paradoxes such as surrendering to fear and even meeting hopelessness. There may come a time when it seems that there is nothing else you can do to make things better beyond superficial levels of comfort and support. Perhaps even those are hampered for various reasons. It may feel as if you are being pushed to the wall. It is understandable to want to avoid suffering, but sometimes it is not the best use of your limited energy and attention to try to hold it at bay or rail against it. "No! This should not be happening!" There may come a time when it would be more beneficial to allow suffering and hopelessness to be part of your experience; to accept the fact that you seem to be completely out of control to make your suffering go away. As counterintuitive as it may sound, when suffering can be received with both hands open, a new horizon may open up. As suffering is opened to consciously – allowed right up close and inside of you – awareness may become apparent, perhaps for the first time, that there is a larger space in which this suffering is taking place, and that the entire fabric of the universe is not suffering. There may be a realization that you are not just the island on which this suffering is taking place, but you are also the vast ocean of abiding awareness that surrounds and enfolds that island. This can be one of the gifts of illness, and it is also an experience of healing.

With the sweetest of intentions, a loved one may counsel us not to give up hope so as not to drown in the quicksand of despair. There are times when this advice is helpful. But there may come a time when even meeting hopelessness is a fruitful choice. Most attempts to change one's life originate from the separate self's attempt to figure out what to do to make life more tolerable, more comfortable. While is it responsible to do what we can to take care of ourselves, let me reassure you that it is not irresponsible to allow hopelessness a seat at the table. It brings its own wise counsel. Often what our mind reaches for are reasons to hope. "I hope this new treatment will work, maybe the pain will get better, maybe the money will come." If these hopes do not come true, oh, what frustration and despair may lie in wait, like a crouching predator! Hope is typically attached to ideas of what we think should happen to change life, to make life better in the future. It is qualified hope. It is partly based on fear of losing control over one's circumstances – or one already feels out of control and is trying to regain it. The nature of this struggle to hold onto hope can breed more frustration and hopelessness.

Beyond the scope of all the mind's ideas of what is hoped for is a resting place, right now, that does not need to be waited for. Hoping can be the very mechanism of delaying peace and well-being when the hoped-for solutions to suffering lie in the realm of "out there, later, maybe." Letting go of hoping, even for a short while, can bring one into "right here, now" just being; not struggling, not waiting for anything to change first. This kind of surrender is not an absence of the intention to heal. It is consciously employing intention to open – to *just this moment, as it is* – to stop fighting against or struggling with what you don't seem able to change. What I have found is that in the present moment there is, deep down, a sense of well-being that is unconditional, meaning it is not a result of anything that might change. It is here in spite of everything – the illness, the debt, the hundreds of reasons one is sure one has a *right* to complain. This is not to say we should not seek solutions, but taking the time to dip into resting *right now* is an option. The cessation of wishing for anything in particular to happen can simultaneously be the arrival into the awareness of peace and unconditional well-being that one has been longing for.

As healing is an intimate personal journey, likewise it is up to each of us to cultivate true inner peace. Someone else's illness may help provide the perfect circumstances for you to get in touch with some illusions you still hold about wanting or needing to be in control of making the world and others "better" in order to feel settled inside. Someone else's illness and your inability to make it better may be a gift for you to grapple with, by which you may come to realize that peace of mind is available regardless of outer circumstances. Notice if someone else's reluctance to take action is triggering any fear in you. Notice if there are ways your attachment to that individual's decisions is precipitating "dis-ease" in your own mind, which then trickles down into ill feelings in your own body. Notice how holding onto ideas about what he or she "ought" to be doing (in your possibly highly informed opinion) is contributing to a down-sliding of health in your own system. Turn the focus around and come back to your own life, sit down in your own seat in the classroom, and do your own "healing homework". Although this may be difficult to accept, no one owes you his or her health, even if it is someone very close to you.

These are ideas I believed, in theory, before diving into recovery from Lyme, but they were frequently reinforced through the process of engaging in my own healing. As I faced arduous challenges within the conscious healing process, there were many moments of realizing how I would never again suppose that anyone else "ought" to undertake such a journey. Yet I would encourage those who are sick, and sick of suffering, to consider the possibility of transformation.

The volition to heal must come from within. Whether through conscious self-reflection or through symptoms of illness that take away your sense of control and limit your activity in the world, one day awareness arises of being in a too-small container, a too-small self-definition. There is something dormant or stuck in a too-small space that wants to be released, to be taken out and aired, to be stretched and fluffed out and brought into the light of day. A foot stuffed into a slipper that is too small, the foot wanting to be free to stretch its toes and run barefoot in the sand and swim in the water. True healing always involves some kind of transformation.

Beyond our little minds, our little selves, there is a vast healing intelligence. We may suspect it and tap into it during periods of creative flow or peak performance, but most of the time, when things are "going well", we credit ourselves with having done something right in order to earn and achieve success, our good health included. Therefore, we may burden ourselves with guilt over personal failure if we become ill or feel defeated. Likewise, we tend to anthropomorphize this "higher power" and believe that we must do something "right" such as saying the right prayer or chanting the right mantra or repeating the right affirmation enough times in order to crack the access code, to deserve its attention, to be allowed to be helped by it. Being defeated seems to prove our lack of success and worthiness. But being confronted with experiences that seem to take away all of our ability to make our lives better may be a blessing in disguise. It invites us to surrender and to see things differently.

Who and what we really are is so much more than these struggling selves in vulnerable physical bodies. On the physical level, everything is impermanent. Physical healing can only ever be temporary. Eventually every *body* is going to die. I have come to shift my focus from a goal of physical healing to cultivating acceptance and awareness of the present moment. I also employ my personal will to be willing to "see things differently" – relinquishing grudges, guilt, the urge to be right, the urge to blame others, the urge to complain, resist, and struggle against my circumstances – in exchange for inner peace. I have found that when my perspective is healed, through dropping judgements against myself, my life, and others, this often precipitates more physical ease, as well as emotional well-being. I have also found that healing includes acknowledging and accepting who I really am at the core, which includes this specific body, as it is, and this character and its unique quirks. Acceptance is maintained through abandoning all idols of an idealized self or life, and by continuing to bring the focus of my attention and awareness back into this very moment, just as it is. Then I reawaken to the awareness of a surrounding, permeating, and in-dwelling presence of well-being, an awareness that serves to support my immune system. This universal spirit or consciousness is also who I really am. ✒

Suggested Reading

Lyme Disease

Joseph J. Burrascano Jr., MD, *Advanced Topics In Lyme Disease: Diagnostic Hints And Treatment Guidelines For Lyme And Other Tick Borne Illnesses*, 2008
Pamela Weintraub, *Cure Unknown: Inside the Lyme Epidemic*, 2009

Healing from Lyme – detailed resource guides

Stephen Harrod Buhner, *Healing Lyme: Natural Healing and Prevention of Lyme Borreliosis and Its Coinfections*, 2005
Katina Makris, CCH, CIH, and Richard Horowitz, MD, *Out of the Woods: Healing from Lyme Disease for Body, Mind and Spirit*, 2014
Kenneth B. Singleton, MD, *The Lyme Disease Solution*, 2008

Autobiography/Biography/Anecdotes about illness and healing

Elizabeth Tova Baily, *The Sound of a Wild Snail Eating*, 2010
Katina Makris, CCH, CIH, *Out of the Woods: Healing from Lyme Disease and Other Chronic Illness–Body, Mind & Spirit*, 2011
Mirabai Starr, translator: *The Interior Castle – Saint Teresa of Avila*, 2003
Bernie S. Seigal, MD, *Love, Medicine and Miracles: Lessons Learned About Self-Healing From a Surgeon's Experience with Exceptional Patients*, 1988

Alternative Healing – information to apply at home or ideas with which to seek professional support

Barbara Ann Brennan, *Hands of Light: a Guide to Healing Through the Human Energy Field*, 1987
Barbara Ann Brennan, *Light Emerging: The Journey of Personal Healing*, 1993
Richard P. Brown, MD, Patricia L. Gerbarg, MD, Philip R. Muskin, MD, *How to Use Herbs, Nutrients, and Yoga in Mental Health Care*, 2009
Dawson Church, Ph.D., *The Genie in Your Genes: Epigenetic Medicine and the New Biology of Intention*, 2007
Deb Soule, *How to Move Like a Gardener: Planting and Preparing Medicines from Plants*, 2013

Awakening, Spiritual Awakening, Consciousness, Inquiry

Adyashanti, *The End of Your World: uncensored straight talk on the nature of enlightenment*, 2008
Adyashanti, *Falling into Grace: insights on the end of suffering*, 2011
Adyashanti, *The Way of Liberation, a practical guide to spiritual enlightenment*, 2012
Adyashanti, *The Impact of Awakening*, 2013
Pema Chödrön, *Taking the Leap: Freeing Ourselves from Old Habits and Fears*, 2010
Pema Chödrön, *When Things Fall Apart: Heart Advice for Difficult Times*, 2011
Jeff Foster, *An Extraordinary Absence: Liberation in the Midst of a Very Ordinary Life*, 2009
Jeff Foster, *The Deepest Acceptance: Radical Awakening in Ordinary Life*, 2012
Jeff Foster, *Falling in Love with Where You Are*, 2013
Jan Frazier, *When Fear Falls Away: The Story of a Sudden Awakening*, 2007
Jan Frazier, *The Freedom of Being at Ease With What Is*, 2012
Byron Katie, *Loving What Is: Four questions that can change your life*, 2002
Byron Katie, *A Thousand Names for Joy: Living in Harmony with the Way Things Are*, 2007
Eva Pierrakos, *The Pathwork of Self-Transformation*, 1990
Gary Renard, *The Disappearance of the Universe: Straight Talk about Illusions, Past Lives, Religion, Sex, Politics, and the Miracle of Forgiveness*, 2004
Gary Renard, *Your Immortal Reality: How to Break the Cycle of Birth and Death*, 2006
Gary Renard, *Love Has Forgotten No One: The Answer to Life*, 2013
Rita Marie Robinson, *Ordinary Women, Extraordinary Wisdom: The Feminine Face of Awakening*, 2007
Nouk Sanchez and Tomas Vieira, *Take Me To Truth: Undoing the Ego*, 2007
Eckhart Tolle, *The Power of Now: a guide to spiritual enlightenment*, 1999
Eckhart Tolle, *A New Earth: Awakening to Your Life's Purpose*, 2005

Acknowledgements

Regarding the original art exhibit and Lyme-Light book, first, I offer my warmest gratitude to my family, friends, and community for your emotional, financial, and artistic support – this project has been a joint venture, with several people playing more than one important role. This is by no means an exhaustive list. In particular, thank you Mary and Paul Gloger for joining me in the difficult yet amazing process of revisiting and revaluing the past. Thank you Paul Gloger for your impeccable editing support. Thank you Andreas Doerfler, and Mary Gloger for your invaluable design, editing, layout, and marketing advice. In the beginning, thank you career counselors Glenon Friedmann and Jill Barlow-Kelly for telling me to "rest first" – the paintings soon followed. Thanks artist, art teacher, and Lyme survivor Ernie McMullen for your advice to seek medical help *and* to explore painting even with "brain fog"! Thank you reporters Jessica Bloch, Bob Evans, Donna Gold, Robert Levin, and Nan Lincoln for your sensitive coverage of the original Lyme-Light exhibit. Thank you Susan Lerner, Terry Watson, Arthur and Carol Westing, Ed Snyder, and everyone who signed the exhibit guest log, for assuring me this work was of value and should be widely shared. Thank you Aaron Steiner and Andreas Doerfler for designing, hosting, and managing the Lyme-Light website. Thank you Jane Karker, president of Maine Authors Publishing, for your professional enthusiasm and personal conviction that this work should also be shared as a book, and to MAP's art director David Allen. Kind regards to the woman at the Appalachian Mountain Club on Echo Lake who stayed at the table and listened, helping me find my bearings to begin the book project. Thank you doctor, teacher, author and Lyme survivor Pat Gerberg for writing the fantastic foreword to usher it in. My creative work also rests on a foundation of support from my community on Mount Desert Island, and friends and family far and near who have helped me find perspective, comfort, courage, and humor during sickness and in health – especially Aubrey Bart, John Bart, Regina Bernhardt, Ann Bohrer, Dennis Bracale, Hana Bracale, Danette Burchill, Georgia Douillet, Dawn Dreisbach, Sue Haynes, Betsey Holtzmann, Yvonne Maiden, Margarita Marnik, Heather Nuesslein, Pam Roland, Aaron Steiner, and Phyllis Weliver. Hugs to my "Lyme Sisters" Meg Burden, Malia and Rose Demers, Nina Devenney, Beth Lambert, and Daaby Tingle, and the late Kirsten Stockman. Thanks to Lisa Burton and Chris Vincenty of Reel Pizza for hosting the movie fundraiser, and cheers to everyone who came. My well-being has also been supported by the care of healers and counselors who have helped me find comfort and alignment on many levels. Thank you Kathleeen Bowman, Michael Curless, Steve Curtin, Anna Durand, Diane Fehrenbach, Matt Gerrish, Jessie Greenbaum, Linette Grindal, Julie Havener, Sandy Bart Heimann, Cecily Judd, Kathleen Kotas, Deborah Loftus, Sheridy Olson, Deborah Page, Dan Torinus, Charly Weir, and Susan Whittaker. I am most grateful to doctor Meryl Nass, whose encouragement and professional care helped restore my ability and willingness to be here.

Regarding this book: Thank you to everyone who encouraged me to produce a revised and updated edition. Thank you Katina Makris for writing *Out of the Woods: Healing Lyme Disease–Body, Mind & Spirit*, which reinforced for me that it can be "for the good of the all" to share our stories of healing. Thank you Carol and Arthur Westing for your ongoing interest in this project, for bringing the exhibit to Vermont, and for your essential editorial support! Thank you Happy Dickey and Beatrice Szantyr of MaineLyme for the excellent "Tick Talks" you have offered. Thank you Jennifer May for your incredible intuitive insights and healing support! Thank you Dr. Blake Rosso, D.C. for your feedback and encouragement and for joining our community as a Lyme-experienced healer with an open-hearted attitude and open-minded intelligence. Thank you Sheila Perloff Eddison of "A Stone's Throw to Health–Ferment" for getting me started on fermented vegetables. Thank you Chris Brown for all the free Food for All community suppers which helped my budget and writing time, and for introducing me to Japanese Knotweed. Thank you Chris Whitten for helping me harvest more of it and teaching me about other healing plants. Thank you Roz Kreilkamp for listening and encouraging me through so many significant decisions. Thank you Dennis Kiley for witnessing and honoring my process and helping me see it in a spiritual light. Thank you Dawn Dreisbach for wonderful discussions about our spiritual realities and for sharing insights from your own experiences of healing. Thank you Theo Welton for shining the spotlight on our capacity to heal from within. Thank you D.U. book group members Mary Lois Allison, Amy Gillis, Sue Haynes, Margarita Marnik, and Kim O'Brien, for helping me "turn the table on the ego" and "forgive the illusion" – while eating delicious food in kind company! Thank you Gaia Diedricksen for your confidences, I thought of you as I was writing this book, best wishes for healing! Thank you Lily Kapiloff for filling the house with live music! Thank you Steve Bohrer for the unexpected dance of loving relationship! Thank you dear John and Hana for providing me with the biggest reasons to keep my feet on the ground as well as opportunities to be playful!

About the Author and Artist

photo by Milena Rodriguez

Emily Bracale is a graduate of the Interlochen Arts Academy and College of the Atlantic, with a B.A. in Human Ecology. Her visual arts training began in early childhood within a clan of three generations of women artists and art teachers. She has taught and supported the creativity of thousands of students from preschool through the college level, in private and public schools, in summer camps, and independently. She has held many solo art exhibits with an educational twist, most notably the "Lyme-Light" collection and "Visions of the World" – cultural travel sketches and paintings. Her watercolor still lifes, landscapes, and seascapes are in private collections in the USA and abroad. She lives with her family in Bar Harbor, Maine. www.facebook.com/inthelymelightbook

www.inthelyme-light.com